ES

For my daughter Ann who carefully checked all my proofs

British Library Cataloguing in Publication Data

Hewison, Christian H
  Shedmaster to railway inspectorate.
  1. Hewison, Christian H
  2. Railroad engineers – Great Britain –
  Biography
  I. Title
  625.1′0092′4   TF140.H/

ISBN 0–7153–8074–5

Photoset by
Northern Phototypesetting Company Bolton
and printed in Great Britain
by Biddles Limited, Guildford
for David & Charles (Publishers) Limited
Brunel House Newton Abbot Devon
Published in the United States of America
by David & Charles Inc
North Pomfret Vermont 05053 USA

Contents

Introduction

This book, which describes the railways as I saw them through over half a century of railway service, portrays them, and, particularly, LNER locomotives and running shed life, from the inside. Yet in telling the story first hand it is inevitable that some long held sacred myths about Gresley locomotives will be exploded, for here there is no place for the flattery and hero-worship adopted by so many authors who have written about the LNER and its first CME, Sir Nigel Gresley. From the start the LNER management had no easy task; six companies and their staff had to be integrated, often with high opinions of themselves, and some jealous and scornful of others. Up to the day of nationalisation there were former GNR officers who had no use whatever for men other than those who had been in GNR service. Money was short throughout the LNER era, the disaster which road transport brought to the railways having begun even before the LNER came into existence; as a result, life in the employment of the company was continually dampened by overruling principles of 'economy'. Nevertheless, there could have been no finer career for me than that of a railwayman.

I had to make two great decisions in my time. One, at the age of 16, was to take up railway engineering as a profession. The second was at a much later date, when I was at Rugby and where one day, in a rather large bookshop, I saw amongst the people there a girl whose appearance completely took my attention from the purpose of my call. I do not think I have ever seen such a beautiful girl as on that day and I lost little time in making her acquaintance; her name was Irene and it is sufficient to say that we were engaged within three months and married three months later. It has been mostly with her loving care and attention that I have been able to follow with success the later and more important half of my railway career which has lasted almost 53 years, and it is mainly to her that this book is dedicated. It is also dedicated, however, to my daughter Ann, who rendered considerable assistance by reading and checking my typescript and proofs, a task of many hours.

December 1980   C. H. Hewison

1 Apprentice

Most boys at some time enjoy running a model railway which, if only in imagination, takes the part of the real thing. A few have the luck to be able to run real railways all their lives and I have been one of them. The railwaymen who taught me my work over many years were grand chaps, so eager to pass their skills on to younger men; there was none of the sad meanness sometimes flaunted in recent times by men who 'go slow', refuse to start trains or disrupt station working because they cannot get their way over a grievance which ought to be sorted out by negotiation.

I was born at Worsborough Dale, Barnsley, in 1909 where my father was a curate. In 1913 he became vicar of Thurgoland, a large scattered Pennine village near Barnsley; the GCR Manchester to Sheffield line that followed the Don Valley passed through the parish. Half a mile from the vicarage Rumtickle Viaduct carries the line over the Don, the odd name dating from about 1840 when a cottage, one in a row, became a tavern named the Rest & Be Thankful, where the masons and navvies who built the viaduct and the tunnel nearby might quench their recurrent thirsts. The men, mostly illiterate, learned the name by hearsay and contorted it into Rumtickle; the cottage group is still so named by the modern Ordnance Survey map.

The engineer of this historic line was Joseph Locke who became President of the Institution of Civil Engineers in 1858; after his death in 1860 the Institution wanted a memorial statue to be set up in Westminster but Locke had dabbled in politics and

London, his rivals insisted, was not the place for it. So his widow bought 17 acres of land in Barnsley that became Locke Park, and the statue stands there instead; a similar statue may be seen in France beneath Locke's great railway viaduct at Barentin, near Rouen.

From an early age railways and railway events fascinated me. So too did the various types of rail transport and their safety aspects, in which I gradually became more interested, little realising that rail safety would be an important part of my later career. When I was only five years old, my father and I explored the disused coal branch that left the main line at a place where Thurgoland station once stood, until it was closed in 1847; its first 300 yards ascended an incline that had obviously been rope worked, as, alongside the A629 road, a stationary engine house's remains were visible. The line, two miles long and ending at a colliery, was closed in 1875 but its formation can still be followed.

On 4 February 1916 our newspapers, printed in Leeds, failed to arrive, the train service from Leeds having been stopped by the collapse of the L&YR Penistone Viaduct over the River Don. The 29 arch viaduct, dating from 1850, stood nearly 100 feet above the river; heavy rains had caused scouring around the foundations of the pier supporting the first and second arches at the Penistone end. On 3 February a tank engine was going on to the viaduct at 4.15pm to cross from one track to the other when the driver saw the rails ahead beginning to bend. He and his fireman jumped from the footplate and ran back only a few seconds before the pier slid into the river, the arches and engine going with it. My parents took me to see the damage; as the line provided a direct Huddersfield to Marylebone passenger service, the L&YR rebuilt the arches within a few months.

Towards the end of 1916 my father became vicar of Marr, a village on the A635 road, four miles from Doncaster, the move being his last until he retired in 1944 and also one that decided my career.

Early in 1925 my father approached the LNER, asking about

the prospects of a career in the Doncaster Railway Works, known as the 'Plant', and we were granted an interview by Mr F. Wintour, the Mechanical Engineer. Gresley, the Chief Mechanical Engineer, had five such MEs, at Doncaster, Stratford, Darlington, Gorton and Cowlairs, until about 1927 when the Doncaster ME was given the supervision of both Doncaster and Gorton; Wintour controlled the locomotive, carriage and wagon works at Doncaster and their respective managers. On the great day my father and I arrived in good time for a 2.0pm appointment at his headquarters where we were kept in a waiting room two hours; then the mighty man received us, without a word of explanation or regret for the delay, a show of disgracefully bad manners or perhaps no manners at all, that I suppose was intended to impress us. I learned later that he was customarily vulgar and rude to people but while seated with a parson as on this occasion he behaved himself. It was resolved that when I had passed an examination of his prescribed standard I could enter the LNER service as a premium apprentice in the Locomotive Works. I left school there and then, studied at home for six months and passed the half dozen papers at the end of the year. I could not foresee, then, that I was going to have to face and pass over a hundred more examination papers before I qualified as an engineer.

On 1 February 1926 I reported to the Plant, commencing my $52\frac{1}{2}$ years' railway career, and was put to work in the Top Turnery, full of men working hard at a great variety of machines amidst much noise. My first assignment was at the marking off tables, steel slabs with polished upper surfaces and absolutely level. Forgings or castings of smaller locomotive parts were prepared for machining by being whitewashed (I was the whitewasher) and then placed on the tables where two highly skilled men scribed the outlines, using spirit levels and set squares and copying from the official blueprints. A month later I was transferred to a lathe gang and given a machine of my own, and soon learned to turn simple components; this was followed by short spells on a slotter, which carried a tool similar to that of a lathe but applied it vertically, and on a shaper that worked in the same way but horizontally. I was also allowed, under supervision, to work a milling machine, a large appliance with a big sliding table that passed a piece of work, or several pieces at once, slowly beneath a revolving cutter. Cutting tools were kept and maintained in a tool room where the men showed me how to sharpen tools and twist drills correctly and how to shape special tools accurately for cutting screw threads.

On 4 May 1926 the General Strike began when almost every industrial trade union in the country called for a stoppage in support of the coal miners who were already on strike against a reduction in pay. The railways and all the railway works came to a halt; volunteers and a handful of loyal railwaymen ran a few trains here and there, and the premium apprentices were sent to Doncaster locomotive running shed, known as the 'Carr'. Although we had never been on engines before we cleaned boiler tubes, took out tapered plugs, filled boilers, replugged and lit up, all on our own responsibility; we moved engines about the depot, shunted wagons and coaled tenders, and it is remarkable that as we muddled along we avoided dreadful accidents. Some of the senior apprentices went out as firemen.

The Strike lasted only ten days but its effects and those of the coal strike on the LNER were catastrophic. One third of the company's revenue came from coal haulage and as the miners' strike went on until it collapsed in the autumn the directors were forced by sheer lack of money to declare a four-day week for the Plant; it was 28 March 1927 before full time was resumed. The railways never forgave their men who had joined the General Strike; their records were endorsed and in later years they were sometimes reminded of the blot on their papers. At the running sheds where mineral engines were laid up by the dozen because there were no coal trains, hundreds of cleaners and firemen who had been on strike were told on returning that they would be notified when they could resume duty; some had to wait two or three years, the strike having transferred to hauliers' lorries much rail goods traffic that was never retrieved.

After six months with machines came a place at a bench where I learned how to use a file properly and realised that the rest of my apprenticeship was going to be spent either filing or plying the locomotive fitter's two basic tools, the hammer and the cold chisel. The men warned me never to apply a file across a narrow strip of steel, an action that would break off the file's teeth, and I learned, too, to keep files for brass separate from those for steel. For some curious reason a new file will cut brass effectively but once used on steel it will never cut brass again although it will continue to cut steel efficiently the rest of its life.

The apprentices had to find out most things for themselves and one day I approached my chargeman and uttered the *dreadful* word, 'Joe, what is a *bastard* file?' His limited information was, however, 'well, now, I'll tell yer, lad; a bastard file is a file that's neither one thing nor t'other!' That was hardly adequate for a trainee engineer and I had to do some research. Engineers' files and rasps have been classified by the British Standards Institution which publishes a booklet listing them. There are eight types for ordinary manual work, named Flat, Hand, Halfround, Round, Square, Threesquare, Warding and Knife, all subdivided into three classes called Bastard, Second Cut and Smooth. The Bastard is the coarsest (there is no such thing as a 'rough' file) and then comes Second Cut followed by Smooth; all files are to be had in a large range of lengths.

The Doncaster Works men were a jolly crowd. Workmen generally had not then been 'made aware of their grievances' by agitators, and the shop steward had not yet appeared; responsibility to their employer was their uppermost thought. There was little supervision because hardly any was needed, the men working steadily at their duties and seldom seeing their foreman unless something needed his decision; the works manager was noticed perhaps once a month when he strolled quietly through the shops.

The first week in September every year was Doncaster Race Week, when the locomotive and carriage works were closed and most of the men went on holiday; railway shopmen did not get leave with pay in those days and the annual Race Week was the only whole week off that they had. During the previous week as many carriage sidings as possible were cleared of rolling stock and made available to the Traffic Department. Race Week traffic in the 1920s was a feat of organisation; 73 special trains arrived at Doncaster on St Leger Day 1927 and had to be handled without disturbing the normal East Coast main line services. Of the total, 32 came from the north, 20 from the south and 21 from the Sheffield direction, worked by a variety of LNER and LMS locomotives. Trains from the north entered the works carriage sidings, the racegoers alighting *without* the advantage of platforms. Engines were turned, serviced and replenished with water in the locomotive works; those from the south were accommodated in the Bentley Colliery sidings and those from Sheffield in sidings at St James's Bridge. In addition, over 1,000 horseboxes were received and despatched during the 1927 race period.

So far I had worked on new engine components but after my second year I was transferred to the erecting shop for repaired locomotives, known as the Crimpsall; with accommodation in four main bays for 100 engines it was one of the largest erecting shops in the country. Its output in 1927 was about 50 engines a month but in the following year there was a reorganisation and the time for an engine's general repair was reduced from two months to three weeks. In that period an engine was stripped of every part, including its boiler, until only the frames and cylinders were left, the boiler was repaired or renewed, all the components were renovated in the machine and fitting bays within the Crimpsall, and the engine rebuilt. Works shunting engines moved the locomotives to the Crimpsall and thence after repairs to the paint shop; there were three of them and one, unofficially named *Alice* by the men, was a GNR 0-4-4 bogie well tank engine built in 1876, originally No 533 and the only one left of its class; it had been fitted with a 5 ton crane for which, apparently, there had never been any use as no one I met had ever seen it in action.

My first Crimpsall assignment was in a connecting rod gang that repaired inside rods; there were only five of us, just a chargeman, a fitter and three apprentices. We had to make each strap a firm sliding fit onto its rod, then fit new half brasses at each end and put in new bolts and a new cotter; every bit of the work had to be done by hand and it was mostly chipping and filing. Never before or since have I filed so much brass and steel; we were allowed *one* new file a month, in exchange for an old one, and we tried to keep two, using them four weeks on brass and then four on steel, the LNER issuing Threesquare files as with only three cutting faces they were cheaper than Square files. How the three faces of those files had to be nursed to make them last! It took one of us a week's hard work to recondition a pair of connecting rods.

After short spells with injector, vacuum brake and safety valve gangs I was put onto the engines themselves, a transfer known as 'being sent to the pits'. Each main bay had four long pits, with room for three Pacifics or about five smaller engines, and each with a chargeman. An engine was basically erected by two fitters, two mates and two apprentices but the chargeman often rearranged his work force, sometimes finishing an engine quickly by concentrating everyone on it. As the men were on piecework, speed became more important than workmanship which was often pretty rough; if predrilled bolt holes in a smokebox did not match holes in a cylinder casting they were made to do so by hammering in a drift.

Every completed engine turned out of the Crimpsall was inspected by a fitter apparently selected for having radar eyesight; he invariably presented the chargeman with a long list of small missing details, parts wrongly assembled or wrong parts assembled, all of which had to be rectified. Before being returned to the Running Department every repaired passenger engine had a trial run of 100 miles or so in the hands of special drivers, and defects that they reported had to be rectified too. Premium apprentices were allowed to go on these trials if they had erected the engines.

11

During 1927 three Pacifics were modified in order to improve their efficiency and power, and I had the good luck to work on all of them in turn as the alterations were made. The first was No 4480 *Enterprise* which was to have its tractive effort raised from 29,835 lb to 36,465 lb. The valve travel was increased by nearly an inch and a new 220 lb/sq in boiler was fitted, 40 lb higher than before; a larger superheater with a wider header was provided. When the fitters attempted to put the smokebox into place it would not go over the header and managers and draughtsmen hurried to the Crimpsall to hold a hasty consultation; it was decided to cut two square holes in the smokebox wrapper plate and to cover them with lids that would enclose the header ends; the lids became standard fittings on later engines. They can be seen today on preserved Gresley locomotives.

Next came No 2544 *Lemberg,* to be given somewhat different modifications; it too received a 220 lb/sq in boiler but had its cylinder diameters reduced from 20 to $18\frac{1}{4}$in. The cylinders were rebored and when cast iron liners of the correct inside diameter had been made for them the two outer cylinders were dealt with, the liners being forced into place by great screws made for the purpose; when the middle cylinder's turn came the exhaust passage casting was found to be in the way and the liner could not be positioned so that it would enter. The draughtsmen who had overlooked that the middle cylinder had more upward tilt than those outside again went into conference with the managers. They decided to cut a great piece out of the casting and then as soon as the liner was in to close the hole with a specially moulded cover, attached by studs and nuts. The changes made on the third engine, No 2555 *Centenary,* were less spectacular; it was given a longer valve travel but retained its 180 lb/sq in boiler. All three engines were then tested and the design of ten new Pacifics built at Doncaster in 1928 was based on the results.

Two or three times a year the premium apprentices visited other works; one of the outings was to Leeds to inspect the 2–6–2 Kitson Still tank engine, an experimental locomotive that, alas, was not very successful. It had eight horizontal cylinders driving a common crankshaft that turned the driving wheels through gears; the cylinders were designed for internal combustion at their outer ends and steam at the piston gland ends; the idea was that once steam had been generated in the somewhat small boiler by an oil burner the heat from the internal combustion exhaust passing through the boiler on its way to the chimney would then maintain steam pressure. Semi perpetual motion had arrived on the railway! A few pathetic tests were made on LNER lines and then the curtain was lowered on the engine which was seen no more.

In 1928 the LNER offered to apprentices a scholarship scheme that amounted to three years' leave of absence with pay to enable them to take a full time University course. There was a competitive examination which I took, winning one of the scholarships and choosing to read Civil Engineering at Sheffield University where I started my first year in October. The Civil Engineering Department was under Professor J. Husband who was about the best lecturer any student could have wished for and he instructed us on foundations, steelwork, bridges, railway construction, permanent way, waterworks, concrete and surveying.

Throughout my three years at Sheffield I had to spend every vacation in the works but the management allowed me to do very much as I liked and I enjoyed spells in the pattern shop, foundry, forge, and with the millwrights. At the University Engineering Society's meetings I heard about local engineering history of which around Sheffield there was a good deal to be learned; the countryside around Barnsley, however, I found to be a treasure house of industrial archaeology. There were Newcomen colliery pumping engines at Elsecar, Rawmarsh and two at Kilnhurst of which one, in 1928, was still at work. Invented by Thomas Newcomen in about 1700, these engines had a piston in a vertical cylinder that worked a vertical pump rod through the medium of a rocking beam; the piston was forced up by low pressure steam and then pushed down by atmospheric pressure when the steam was condensed by cold water causing a partial vacuum in the cylinder. The Elsecar engine, which worked from about 1795 to 1923 at six strokes a minute, has been preserved by the National Coal Board and is the only Newcomen engine in the country still on the site where it was first installed; it stands about four miles south-east of Barnsley, alongside the B6097 road.

Less than a mile from Thurgoland, the Wortley Top Forge lies beside the Don; dating from 1620 and one of the oldest ironworks in Yorkshire, it is under restoration and is scheduled as an Ancient Monument. It contains a helve hammer raised by a water wheel and falling by its own weight, striking about 20 times a minute.

The canals around Barnsley were constructed nearly 200 years ago, when coal mining began in south Yorkshire; long since disused and abandoned, their routes can still be followed. Several short branches terminated at basins to which tramroads of the early plateway type brought coal from mines a few miles away; one of them, $3\frac{1}{2}$ miles in length and opened in 1809, ran from a basin at Barnby on the A635 Road, and at places along the route the original stone sleepers are still to be seen, particularly at Silkstone, two miles from Junction 37 on the M1 Motorway. I called the tramroad 'The Silkstone Railway' in my article in the 1937 *Railway Magazine*.

Living in a mining area, I could occasionally obtain a surreptitious inspection of a colliery winding engine on a Saturday afternoon. These are the engines that manipulate the cages up and down the shafts, and few people can ever see them as, unlike locomotives, they are contained in an engine house and worked in conditions of the strictest privacy. If the engine driver is the aristocrat of the railway, the winder is the grand duke of the mine for a colliery's output depends on the rate at which he can bring the coal to the surface, and the lives of men who are going down the pit are in his hands.

The engines in the Doncaster area generally had two horizontal cylinders and were huge, often with 6ft piston strokes; some are still working although electric winding gear is superseding them. The connecting rods turn a crankshaft on which is mounted the rope barrel of up to 20ft in diameter. The ropes that carry the cages are wrapped around the barrel in opposite directions so that as the overlap rope is paid out its place is taken by the underlap rope being drawn in. Indicators show the winder the cage positions and he works to orders from an onsetter at the bottom of the shaft who signals '1 – raise', and from a banksman at the top who then signals '2 – lower'. Colliery winding is a very involved and exact science; the equipment has many safety devices, accidents are rare and a pit cage is one of the safest carriages in which to ride.

I was sent for my second summer University vacation to Carr running shed, where some 200 locomotives were maintained, to learn how they were kept in service. Not only were day to day running repairs carried out but certain parts of the engines were given periodical examinations; water gauges were dismantled and checked monthly, as were injectors and vacuum brake cab fittings, and every six months the pistons and valves were taken out and inspected. I passed the summer with the fitters who dealt with this work, spent a few weeks with the boilersmiths and then had a spell with the fitters who did small immediate repairs to engines that were at the shed only an hour or two for fire cleaning and coaling, and who carried out most of their work under dreadful conditions. They tried to tighten glands and pipe joints in clouds of scalding steam, going beneath engines on outdoor tracks not provided with pits, or working in dense and filthy smoke. 'If they put animals in this ***** shed' one fitter remarked, 'the ***** Directors would be hauled up before the beaks by the RSPCA!' In winter, in thick fog and heavy frost, they worked both day and night shifts and were expected despite bitter cold or pouring rain to adjust brakes, pack glands and correct faulty sanding gear on engines in the open. What happened when conditions were bad was obvious; the repairs just didn't get done.

Then I was given an engine pass and sent out as a fireman, first on shunting engines, then on goods trains and finally on Pacifics working express trains from Doncaster to King's Cross. Apprentices did not replace the regular firemen but travelled as a third man; they did spells of firing, however, at the driver's discretion and learned how to work the boiler injectors. I soon realised that to fire an engine properly one needed a sound knowledge of the engine's own ability to make steam, of the train's weight and of the gradients along the route; firing a Pacific to London and back, maintaining continuously all the steam that the driver needed, preserving the proper water level in the boiler and reducing the fire towards the end of the run so that there would be next to nothing left on the grate by the time the engine returned to the shed, called for considerable skill.

After finishing my three years at Sheffield I did more fitting and firing at Carr shed. No one troubled in the least where I went with my engine pass, of which I made the most; I explored all the lines in Lincolnshire, around Nottingham and in the West Riding of Yorkshire, including the main line of the former Hull & Barnsley Railway. I was sent to Mexborough for a few weeks; the LNER Garratt was stationed there and I had two or three days on its footplate, banking heavy Manchester bound mineral trains up the 1 in 40 Worsborough Branch. Mexborough also had the S1 class engines; they were GCR 0–8–4 tank locomotives of which one, No 6171, had a booster fitted to the bogie. They propelled long rafts of coal wagons up the hump in the Wath marshalling yard and had three cylinders so that they would not stall in any of the dead centre positions; the booster was intended to increase No 6171's tractive or, I should say, pushing effort but whether the enginemen ever used it was questionable. One driver said that it gobbled so much steam that it left the main cylinders short.

Towards the end of 1931 I was put in the Doncaster Drawing Office and given a few locomotive drawings to prepare; I had done draughtsman's work in the University drawing office but here, at last, I was doing real locomotive design. The office was Gresley's favourite and almost every engine built until then under his jurisdiction had been designed there or, after 1923, in a similar office at Darlington. It was staffed by a group of competent and devoted but grossly underpaid men; I suppose the chief draughtsman, and his second in command had reasonable salaries but many of the men at the drawing boards were receiving fitters' wages or very little more. The huge wooden drawing boards and clumsy wooden T squares were comparable with James Watt's equipment of 150 years earlier and the office methods were archaic. When I found lumps of chalk being scraped to produce dust that would make the tracing linen take the Indian ink I bought a sixpenny tin of talcum powder and applied that instead but my innovation caused the chief draughtsman the deepest distress; he *claimed* that he objected to the *scent* but the real offence was that I had tried to introduce a *new idea* into his office! He was more displeased still when I reminded him that the Doncaster Drawing Office had been the last in the world to cling to the single driving wheel engine, having produced the final 4–2–2 locomotives in the year 1900. The office motto seemed to be, I told him, that 'what our grandfathers did we will perpetuate to our utmost!' It was as well for me that Gresley was not around that day.

2 Engine Sheds – GN and CLC

New England, on the northern outskirts of Peterborough, was the location of a running shed similar in size to Carr depot, having about 200 engines. Here, in April 1932, I was given my first appointment, in the lowly grade of supernumerary running shed foreman; however, every young man has to start at the bottom, I had at least obtained a salaried situation with probabilities of promotion and I had little previous experience of the work of the Locomotive Running Department that I was entering. A District Running Superintendent (DLS) had his office at the shed; his District consisted of four main sheds, namely New England, Peterborough East, Grantham and Boston, and a few tiny outdepots. Unlike other departments' Districts all of which had clearly defined boundaries, the Locomotive Running Districts did not have any prescribed outlines; a DLS's supervision was over men, not territory.

The LNER was divided into three Areas, named Southern (the former GN, GC and GE systems), North Eastern (the former NER) and Scottish (the former NBR and GNSR); each Area had a Locomotive Running Superintendent (LRS). The Southern Area had 13 Locomotive Districts in 1932, each with a DLS and most of them with an Assistant DLS. Almost every DLS was posted at or very close to a principal shed which saved the management the cost of putting someone specially in charge of it; the Assistant had to supervise the shed in addition to doing such work as his DLS gave him. The other sheds of any size were nearly all managed by running shed foremen, a convenient designation prescribed by the General Manager for belittling their situations so that he could keep down their salaries. Very small sheds housing perhaps one to four or five engines were run by shed chargemen who received little more than workman's pay. On the LNER every shed foreman or chargeman was a man who had served a fitter's apprenticeship.

The entire arrangement was excellent from Gresley's point of view; he designed and built the engines which he then passed to the Running Superintendents on the principle that 'it was up to them to make the engines work'. It was unwise to attribute locomotive failures to errors in design and a DLS or LRS who attempted to do so was likely to learn of Gresley's extreme displeasure; all failures resulted from drivers' mishandling or lack of shed maintenance.

The traffic hauled by New England engines and men was chiefly along the GN main line and consisted mostly of express goods trains and of coal trains from South Yorkshire to London. It is difficult to realise today just how heavy the freight and mineral traffic was on most main lines in the 1930s; although road haulage was developing, the trains still carried enormous consignments, and the main line from Peterborough to London, with four tracks most of the way, was worked to capacity. The two LNER freight Mikado 2–8–2s, the most powerful engines in the British Isles apart from the LNER and LMS Garratts, were allocated to New England and could work 100 wagon coal trains to London, which they did daily but not always successfully. Coal wagons of 50 years ago had three link couplings and belonged mostly to the collieries that despatched the coal or to coal merchants. Their couplings and drawgears were not always of the best and if the Mikado drivers failed to keep the wagon couplings taut a snatch could occur at any place where the gradient changed and break a coupling. This was almost a regular occurrence on the 100 wagon trains causing substantial delays while the front half of the train was reversed and reattached.

My work at the depot was largely that of a technical assistant.

19

I prepared schemes and drawings for small alterations recommended by locomotive inspectors or leading fitters to engine components, and I set out proposed alterations to buildings or track layouts at the various depots in the District. I was given my first Rule Book and its General Appendix, two important books of regulation that, being fresh from the works, I had hardly known to exist. I at once realised that my ignorance of the rules was a serious gap in my railway education and I determined to master the contents of the Rule Book which was not done readily and indeed took some years; it proved its worth later on occasions when I found that because I knew the rules properly I could overthrow cases of alleged lapses on the part of drivers, to the great annoyance, of course, of the Operating people! I little foresaw, on first turning the Rule Book's pages in 1932, that when its contents came to be completely rewritten some 30 years later I would be playing a part in its recasting at the highest level.

To improve my experience I was sent to another depot to stand in for the shed foreman during his leave. This was Retford where the former GC Sheffield to Grimsby main line crossed the GN line on the level; there were two sheds, the GN shed alongside the station and the other, half a mile away, of GC origin. The latter was the more important but had fearfully dilapidated buildings that probably dated from July 1849 when the Sheffield to Grimsby route was opened. I spent most of my time there and made my first acquaintances with GC passenger engines, such as the B4 and B5 4–6–0s; I had a few footplate trips, now being in permanent possession of an engine pass, and one was on a B2 Sir Sam Fay 4–6–0 inside cylinder engine. A Bassett-Lowke catalogue that I had admired ten years earlier depicted a fine Sir Sam Fay; named after the GCR's famous general manager, the first was built in 1912 and was very grand to look at but rather poor in performance. The Director 4–4–0 engines, introduced a year later, were much better, their arrival causing the B2s, six in number, to be banished from the GC London line to Retford and Grimsby. In every 4–6–0 design there is the problem of arranging the ashpan clear of the trailing axle because the middle and rear axles cannot be far enough apart for the firebox and ashpan to hang between them. The B2's rearmost firebars were only about a foot above the rear axle and the back of the ashpan was thus so shallow that ash filled it in no time, impeding the air flow to the grate.

While at Retford I began to learn about running small GN locomotives of types seldom seen at New England; they included Classes J1 to J6 which were six coupled tender goods engines, and D1 and D2 inside cylinder 4–4–0 passenger engines that had once worked expresses from King's Cross. If an engine is to generate steam properly the shed foreman must see to it that his staff service it thoroughly. The ashpan must be empty and the grate free from clinker if air is to reach the fire; the flue tubes must be clean within and on the ends. An engine must not leave the shed with its smokebox choked with 'smokebox ash' which is unburnt fuel that the draught through the fire has carried in particles along the flue tubes, and the smokebox must be airtight. On GN engines the smokebox doors often fitted very indifferently and when they allowed air to leak into the smokebox from outside the ash that gathered there as the engine worked soon caught fire behind the door and then burned a hole through it.

It was during my time at New England that the LNER Directors decided to adopt Gill Sans lettering for every form of printing and for all signboards throughout the system; it was designed by Eric Gill, an eminent sculptor and engraver. Presumably the company had to pay a pretty good fee for his art but the decision of the Directors to employ him at all at a time when the LNER was in a bad financial way, as indeed it certainly was, seems odd; surely the 26 letters of the alphabet and the figures 0 to 9 could have been draughted in any one of the dozens of drawing offices in the CME's and Civil Engineer's Departments. It was not very encouraging to the scores of underpaid draughtsmen to see such work going to someone in private practice.

In 1933 I was given a small depot of my own to manage, at Chester Northgate on the Cheshire Lines Committee's railway. I had 12 engines, all of GC origin, and a steam railcar; the enginemen were most competent, as were the two fitters and the boilersmith who kept the locomotives in order. The CLC system was originally owned jointly and equally by the GCR, GNR and MR, the Committee consisting of nominated directors of the three companies; the LNER thus owned two thirds of the railway and the LMS the rest. It had its own General Manager and staff, and owned nearly 500 carriages, all lettered CLC, but no locomotive running department; the LNER provided the engine power for CLC trains. My depot was supervised by the DLS at Gorton, whose office was in Cornwall Street and close to but not at the large Gorton running shed which, as usual, was run by his Assistant.

My engines worked the 39 mile CLC line to Manchester Central and the LNER line that left the CLC and extended westwards to a triangular junction about six miles away where it merged with the LNER line between Seacombe, on the Mersey estuary, and Wrexham. Near this junction the line from Seacombe crossed the Hawarden Swing Bridge spanning the River Dee, one of the largest railway swing bridges in the country, which still exists. The Northgate to Wrexham trains ran in hopeless competition with the GWR whose route between Chester and Wrexham was $12\frac{1}{2}$ miles in length compared with the 20 miles that the LNER journey involved. The English-Welsh border was just to the north of the swing bridge and the line beyond it to Wrexham was the only piece of LNER main line in Wales. For my passenger trains I had six C14 4–4–2 tank engines with inside cylinders, and very good engines they were, except for an inclination to sustain hot boxes. They had been built in 1907 by J.G. Robinson, the CME of the GCR, and were similar but improved versions of a 4–4–2 tank engine that, as locomotive engineer of the Waterford, Limerick & Western Railway, he had provided for that Company; no doubt he had been impressed by the very first 4–4–2 inside cylinder tank

22

engines, introduced by the Taff Vale Railway in 1888.

To work my goods trains I had four or five N5 0–6–2 tank engines, all of which, however, had continuous brake equipment and so could haul passenger trains. Finally, there was a J63 0–6–0 tank engine with outside cylinders that shunted all day at Connah's Quay on the Welsh bank of the Dee; the men knew it as *The Dido* although how they came to associate it with the Phoenician goddess of that name I never learned. She and six other J63s, built in 1906, were the only 0–6–0 tank engines that the GCR ever possessed.

None of the engines gave very much trouble, to a large extent because they did not have full vacuum brake equipment but only an ejector and a train pipe; GC engines had steam brakes. Occasionally there was a heated axlebox to repair but it was GCR practice to have steel axleboxes with removable brass bearings; the depot had a hoist and all we had to do was to raise the engine sufficiently to withdraw the bearing which could then soon be remetalled, filed true and replaced. All axlebox lubrication was by the simple and effective method of trimmings and oil wells in the axlebox tops; we were spared fancy mechanical outfits that were for ever liable to break down.

The Chester railcar was less simple to keep in operation, however. Its type had better remain nameless but it consisted of a car on two bogies, one containing the four driving wheels and having the engine compartment above it. There was a small driving cab at the other end, and a luggage compartment and a saloon for sixty passengers in the middle. The car ran a service between Northgate and Shotton to connect with the Seacombe-Wrexham service, chugging along at about 20mph on the level; it was just able to crawl at foot pace up a gradient into Northgate station. It was claimed that the car's advantages over a train were that the services of a guard were dispensed with and that its coal consumption was low; unfortunately it used to fail about once a week, when an ordinary train with a guard hurriedly recruited from the station staff then had to take its place; if the defect was not in one of the wretched little boiler injectors or in the boiler itself it would be one discovered by the local carriage and wagon examiner. The boiler was a plague; it had an internal firebox, the two being joined by annular flanges with enormous gaskets between them. In theory the firebox flanges and those on the outer shell were *exactly* the same distance apart; in practice they rarely were or else they were not exactly parallel; closely spaced nuts and studs drew them together but the gaskets often leaked under steam pressure or bits of gasket blew out from between the studs, when the whole affair had to be dismantled, an operation that involved lowering the firebox by means of tackle so that we could fit a new gasket and try again. On the whole, the notion that the car achieved a saving was more wishful than real.

I learned most of my shed management tasks from two faithful old shed enginemen who were drivers confined to the shed premises for health reasons. They showed me how to allocate the engines to the various workings and to arrange the engine crews for them; these crews were pre-rostered on a general basis of a week on a morning turn of duty followed by a week of afternoon or evening work but rearrangements were needed almost daily. I had to ensure that we had supplies of coal on hand, which was not difficult as a Central Coal Office at Doncaster ordered our coal from the collieries and saw to its despatch. I was responsible for sending the Office details of consumption and stocks every day, and being sure that we were not running short, or getting wagons of coal from another depot if we were deficient.

Each engine had to spend 24 hours in the shed weekly for the washing out of its boiler and two engines needed to be set aside for this every day. In hard water areas scale forms in a boiler as in a kettle and unless removed will soon accumulate in the water spaces around the firebox which are only some four inches across; scale that is choking a water space will prevent the water from covering the firebox's inner plate which is invariably of copper and the fire will then begin to overheat the plate and waste the copper away. A copper plate damaged in this manner cannot be repaired; once serious wasting has set in the engine must go to the main works for the removal of the boiler and the fitting of a new firebox, and any shed foreman who allowed such a thing to happen would be in very grave trouble indeed, as he would if the flat top of a firebox, called the crown sheet, became similarly damaged.

All boilers are provided with tapered steamtight brass plugs that screw into the steel outer plates but are readily removed by means of a box spanner. There are also several small removable 'mudhole doors' around the bottom of the water spaces. An engine that is to be washed out is put aside for several hours until the steam pressure has gone and the water cooled; the boiler washer then removes the plugs and mudhole doors, so emptying the boiler completely. Next, he inserts a large hose into one of the upper plug holes in the cab and washes all the loose scale off the crown sheet. Then he goes into the smokebox, puts his hose into the plug holes at that end and washes the boiler barrel until the loose scale has been swept by the water into the firebox water spaces; finally, with plenty of water still flowing, he inserts a rake through the lowermost plug holes and stirs the scale in the water spaces until the water swills it all through the mudhole doorways. He must then look into the water spaces, using a small torch for illumination, to make sure that they are clear; The boilersmith is usually carrying out routine inspections at the same time and he, too, checks the state of the water spaces. With the washout completed, plugs and mudhole doors are replaced and tightened and the boiler washer's last duty is to refill the boiler so that steam can be raised.

On the LNER the boilersmith had to give his shed foreman a form every fortnight, certifying that each boiler was in order; if any defects were appearing he told the foreman whether it was essential for repairs to be carried out at once, before the boiler was steamed again, or whether it would be sufficient if they were done fairly soon; it was vital that the foreman followed the boilersmith's advice. Every six months the boilers were examined by a CME's boiler inspector from Gorton; he would probably inspect two engines on each visit and I had to have them properly prepared for him. He was an excellent fellow, letting me accompany him when he went inside the fireboxes and showing me all the features to which he gave his attention.

There was a card for every engine and another for its boiler on which I had to enter the dates of every fitter's periodical examination of the water gauges, safety valves, injectors, connecting rods, pistons and slide valves, and the dates on which the boilersmith did his examinations. It was for me to see that all these inspections were carried out within scheduled periods; water gauges every month, safety valves every three months, and connecting rods, pistons and slide valves every six months. It took two or three days for one fitter and his mate to deal with a 'pistons and valves' examination.

'Putting the engine away' at the end of each day's work amounted to coaling the bunkers, filling the water tanks and raking the ashes out of the ashpans into the ash pit; one of the shed staff loaded all the ashes into a wagon next day, the filled vehicles being despatched to places where Civil Engineer's men could use the contents for making up ground. One of my responsibilities was to see that the ash pit was properly cleared and another was to ensure that dry sand was available for the engine sandboxes; the sand came loose in wagons and had to be unloaded into a sand house where it was dried over a furnace and poured into a bunker from which enginemen could draw bucketfuls when preparing their locomotives.

Every engine driver had to sign in a book every six months that he was properly acquainted with the routes over which he would have to work; it was my duty to see that they did so and to make sure that each route was known by sufficient men for the depot's requirements, and that they learned or relearned them if necessary. Drivers also had to be issued with a copy of the weekly traffic circulars that gave details of temporary speed restrictions and engineering works, alterations to signals, and modifications to permanent rules and regulations; these, too, had to be signed for by each driver and their issue was regarded as being highly important. Before going off duty drivers were required to enter on repair sheets any defects that had developed on the engines that they had worked; nuts and other fastenings to be screwed up, pipe joints to be tightened, sanding apparatus to be made workable, brake pull rods to adjust and so on. The fitters took the sheets, carried out the necessary work and then initialled the entries to indicate that it had been done. Every engine was given a thorough visual examination by one of the fitters before it was taken from the shed to work a train; both drivers and fitters at Chester looked after their engines well and as a result major repairs were seldom needed.

Two important principles prevail at all depots where locomotives are stabled, and indeed on all railway lines and sidings. One is that an engine may be moved only by a qualified driver, with the exception that in the course of their work fitters may lever engines along a track by means of pinch bars; the other is that no one may do any fitting or maintenance work on a locomotive until red flags, or targets that are usually painted red and lettered 'not to be moved', have first been put on the engine, readily visible, and the hand brake applied and scotches put under a wheel as well. As the foreman, I had to keep an eye on my staff and insist that they were scrupulous about these requirements.

I began to learn that as far as supervisors' pay was concerned the LNER's principle was one of severe and griping economy. By belittling the posts, salaries were kept at the lowest possible levels although it was frequently sermonised to shed foremen that any ideas of seeking extra payment for overtime or Sunday duty ought to be utterly beneath the dignity of men holding positions such as theirs. A General Manager's circular laid down that all employees were free to make any applications in connection with their employment but a supervisor so presumptious as to apply for *extra payment* on good grounds would have had the GM's eye on him for a long time and been likely to find himself anticipating promotion for a long time, too. The standard reply to anyone seeking salary improvements was always that his post 'compared favourably' with others carrying similar pay scales, which was safely and completely unchallengeable. Nevertheless, it was hardly inspiring to see that almost everywhere the Operating Department's stationmasters drew far higher salaries than the shed foremen who worked along with them; 'Operating' was one of the General Manager's darlings – 'Locomotive Running' was not.

Applications for vacant posts were acceptable, however, and I was entitled to submit them; sometimes I obtained interviews and one or two were with the Locomotive Running Superintendent of the North Eastern Area, at York. It is normally un-Christian-like, I know, to speak in the least ill of deceased fellow men *(de mortuis nil nisi bonum)* but in the case of one particular individual who held that post I openly say that if ever the term 'swine' was earned and deserved by any railway officer it was ascribable to this horrible individual in the largest symbols. He had no scruples about making it pretty clear that he preferred applications from single men who could fill his vacancies speedily, unhampered by domestic encumbrances; men who might claim household removal costs, having been so thoughtless as to marry girls of their choice, could seek their chances elsewhere as far as he was concerned. He would bully applicants by asking whether they would be prepared to accept salaries less than those advertised, so getting them into a corner from which there was no escape; he originated from the Great Eastern Railway, a system that rather seems to have been run on such principles.

Promotion to Walton-on-the-Hill depot, also on the CLC and amidst the northern outskirts of Liverpool, came in May 1934. The LNER and LMS companies shared the depot, each keeping about 15 engines there, with footplate and shed staff; although the LNER provided the engines for all CLC trains the LMS used its own engines and men to work trains between CLC and LMS stations and goods depots. A year or two before my arrival the two companies had introduced a unique economy scheme at four shared depots on the CLC, namely Walton, Brunswick (also in Liverpool), Trafford Park and Heaton Mersey. It was called the

Closer Working System, whereby the LNER foreman managed the depot for both companies, supervising their staff and reporting to the respective District Officers. The shed staff were pooled and worked as required on either company's engines, the Accountant's Departments sorting out and allocating the various charges; stores were made common in the same way. The Department which the LNER called Locomotive Running was, on the LMS, known as Motive Power.

The CLC's main line connected Liverpool and Manchester Central stations; another line left it at the Hunt's Cross – Halewood triangle of junctions, seven miles from Liverpool Central, and curved northwards and then westwards, terminating at Huskisson station, named after the Huskisson Dock. Walton station was about $1\frac{1}{2}$ miles from Huskisson with the engine shed alongside the platforms. This route from Hunt's Cross and Halewood was known as the North Docks Extension Line; it was opened as far as Walton on 1 December 1879 and it was unfortunate that on that date the second passenger train to leave Walton, the 8.0am train to Liverpool Central which had eight carriages hauled by MS&LR Engine No 266, collided with MR Engine No 1297 at Brunswick, $1\frac{1}{4}$ miles from Central station, causing the death of one passenger and injuries to five others. The rest of the line to Huskisson, part of which lay through a fairly long tunnel beneath the Liverpool streets, was opened in 1880. By 1934 the passenger service along the Huskisson branch had long since been discontinued, Huskisson having become a very large goods terminal; the up and down platforms at Walton were intact and were used very occasionally for excursion trains.

The staffing arrangements at Walton were that I supervised the shed during the day, assisted by a very willing old shed engineman called Jack Heggarty; LMS running foremen took over at 4.0pm and were in charge of both LNER and LMS affairs until next morning. There were two LMS clerks, it being LMS practice to do much of the District paper work at the sheds, whereas on the LNER similar duties were carried out in the

District Offices. I had all my own LNER correspondence to do myself and all LMS paper work that involved mechanical matters.

Walton did not have any passenger workings. For engines I had, on the LNER side, J10 0–6–0 tender and N5 0–6–2 tank locomotives, both with 5ft 1in wheels and both having tractive efforts of 18,780 lbs; they worked short distance goods trains and shunted at Huskisson. There were also a couple of the larger J11 0–6–0 tender goods engines for working further afield. Three or four goods trains left Huskisson in the late afternoon for York, Colwick and Immingham, worked by Walton men and by Gorton engines that arrived on incoming morning goods trains and were serviced and stabled by my shed staff. These engines were usually Class B7 four-cylinder 4–6–0s which, having 5ft 8in wheels and a tractive effort of 30,000 lb less 50, were powerful units; sometimes they were of the B9 two-cylinder type. The same engines invariably turned up day after day, enabling us to play our part towards keeping them in good order; it was very seldom that any failed in service. Another regular visitor was the Class B8 inside cylinder 4–6–0 No 1349, *Glenalmond;* it came from Colwick and the trains it worked back there were loaded exclusively with tobacco.

The LNER part of the depot was under the DLS at Gorton but as communication between the two places was difficult he left me very much alone; the running of my LNER engines worked well on the whole, except in foggy weather, and the daily routine went along calmly.

By contrast, the LMS structure seemed to be one of utter chaos. It would have been unfair to have judged the entire LMS system by my observations at the Company's tiny Walton outpost but my impression was that what I saw was rather typical. The LMS was highly organised but the supervisors always seemed to be devoting so much effort and exertion to organising the organisation that they had no time to run the railway properly. The four Divisions were considered to be strictly separate and by doing their utmost to keep them so the

LMS managers put a great incubus around their own necks. There was a considerable although intermittent import banana traffic at Huskisson that demanded special LMS trains but I had sufficient engines only for the regular workings. Engines invariably had to be found for banana trains but only the Midland Division was allowed to supply them; unless they could be provided from Heaton Mersey, my nearest Midland Division shed having goods engines, which was seldom possible, they would be sent light from Derby or Sheffield, a most wasteful policy. I cannot say how the empty banana vans came back to Huskisson; I do know that the banana train engines never did.

But if the LMS Officers were chainbound by the Divisional system their engines had no respect for it at all. My goods train engines, all of the 4F 0–6–0 type, roamed around the LMS system far and wide; once a Walton engine had set out on a scheduled Walton working, and on which it should have returned, we never saw it again for weeks and weeks. Somehow we haggled along, using any engines that turned up when all our own were lost. We knew in time where our engines had been because drivers, everywhere, recorded running defects on Repair Cards which were always passed to the shed owning the engine, it being deemed that depot's duty to keep the engine in order. These cards would arrive from London, Glasgow, Aberdeen, Holyhead, or Swansea; indeed, I am sure that I have seen the name of every LMS motive power depot on them at one time or another. There were, of course, properly planned engine diagrams similar to those of the LNER but LMS depots were usually so pressed for locomotive power that as engines arrived they were hurriedly serviced and sent out again, regardless of whether they were being sent towards their home depots or further away from them. Every LMS engine carried its shed number on its smokebox door, the Walton number being 19, changed later to 23F; no one, it seemed, paid much attention to these clues. A weekly return of the 'breakdown of booked workings' was required but I never troubled to send it although Walton workings were breaking down all the time. No one ever asked for the returns and I had no intention of filling in forms merely to keep LMS clerks busy.

The rest of the LMS engines at Walton were for shunting; there were two or three L&Y 0–6–0 saddle tank engines that worked at Langton Dock, two miles away, and four L&Y 'pug' engines which shunted the Mersey Docks & Harbour Board lines. The pugs were of the 0–4–0 saddle tank type with outside cylinders, very small wheels, wooden blocks for buffers and a bell that tolled dismally all the time that the engine was in motion, to conform with the Board's bye-laws. All my L&Y types were given their major examinations at Bank Hall depot and on one occasion after sending a pug there I had a telephone call from the District Officer who received it, asking how it was that the valve gear had become so worn that he could see daylight between the eccentric sheaves and their straps! This was not difficult to explain as most of the dock lines were paved with setts laid level with the rail tops; sand usually lay thick on this paving and, due to the engine's low axles, the eccentrics worked continuously within about three inches of it, picking a good deal of it up. Oil and sand together, I patiently explained, tend to be abrasive.

The LMS company's organisation for sending engines to one of the main works for general repairs every few years was the great Shopping Bureau. The LNER's principle was to call the engines in when they had run the mileage that they were expected to cover between works repairs. At an LMS shed, however, the foreman had to decide initially when it was time for his engines to go to the works and to compile a comprehensive 'shopping proposal'. I used to write out these proposal forms, on which I could enter only information that was generally far too vague to provide the slightest guidance to anybody. 'Condition of valve gear – fair, condition of brake gear – worn, condition of tyres – getting hollow' and so on. The forms were then despatched to the Bureau, conveying this drivel, and a week or two later they would be returned, rubber stamped with 'repropose in 3 months time' or something similar. Many engines had to be reproposed two or three times before the works

Above: Joseph Locke's statue in Locke Park, Barnsley. *Below:* Cromford & High Peak Railway; stone sleepers of 1831 to be seen at Parsley Hay.

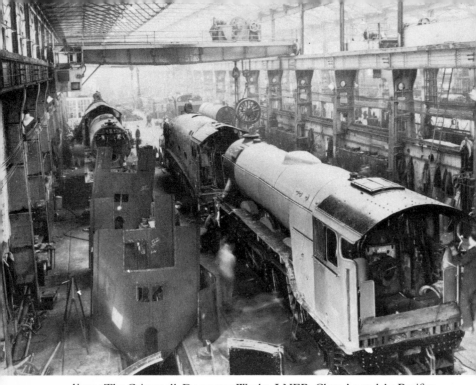

Above: The Crimpsall, Doncaster Works, LNER. Class A3 and A4 Pacifics under repair. (*National Railway Museum*). *Below:* The new erecting shop, Doncaster Works, LNER. Class V4 2–6–2 No 3401 is seen under construction. (*National Railway Museum*).

eventually took them, and very careful one had to be when proposing on a second or third occasion to make sure that every part was described as being a little more worn than before. Eventually an order arrived for the 'proposed' engine to be taken out of traffic, followed by another directing its despatch to Derby, Horwich or Crewe works.

When I was not engaged on LMS engine arrangements I and the clerks were busy trying to keep pace with the sheaves of printed instructions and demands for information that descended on us from LMS headquarters. It was clear from the mass of paper that circulated around the LMS complex that clerical staff were making work for one another by inventing problems and then sending letters and requesting data in the pretence of seeking solutions. I am sure that many of the numerous LMS returns that I had to submit were merely contributions to statistics that were neither necessary nor ever put to any useful purpose.

In winter we had spells of fog of a severity not seen nowadays; I have known dense fog to persist continuously at Liverpool three or four days on end, so thick that a man's range of vision was two yards at the most. Goods trains became hopelessly delayed under such conditions and the arrangement of enginemen's duties became a most difficult task; somehow we managed and the men themselves were accustomed to all kinds of bad weather; it is greatly to their credit that collisions and other accidents in sidings and goods depots during dense fog by day and in even more difficult conditions on foggy nights were almost unknown.

Brunswick depot provided engines for the CLC main line; it was a horrible hole, on a site that had been quarried out of a tall red sandstone cliff and reached only by a flight of 97 steps descending from a street, anyone who cycled to work having to carry his bicycle down these steps and up again. The depot was more important than Walton although no better in amenities, and I was sent there twice to act for the shed foreman during his leave. The whole shed was perpetually enveloped in foul smoke that even penetrated into the dark grimy cells that served as offices. The LMS had only two or three engines there and about half a dozen men; on the LNER side there were D9 4–4–0 engines that worked the popular CLC hourly passenger service between Liverpool and Manchester, of which the Brunswick drivers and their colleagues at Trafford Park were very proud, and rightly so as it was the best of the three services between the two cities, the 34 miles being covered in 45 minutes. There was also the usual pool of goods and shunting engines, and a few tank engines for the somewhat infrequent service between Liverpool Central and Southport.

Walton was one of the LNER's lesser known sheds but it became prominent once a year, on Grand National Day when as many as 30 race specials from the Midland lines and from the LNER arrived at the CLC's Aintree station, every engine coming to Walton for turning, coaling and servicing. The Aintree Race Week started for me about the previous Friday when a horsebox special came from Newmarket, worked all the way by a Great Eastern type engine in the hands of March men with a conductor. On National Day I had to be prepared to receive some 30 engines almost all at once, at about 1.30pm, and to get them serviced but without interrupting the ordinary daily engine routine of the depot; fortunately I had old Heggarty who understood the Grand National from previous years and most of the drivers who brought the 'race' engines in knew exactly what they had to do. It was inferred on my first 'National Day' by a locomotive inspector posted at Aintree that the promptness of the turnround would be seen as an indication of my general abilities to carry out running shed duties in a smart and lively manner. The turnround was not particularly rapid, however, as the engines, including an LNER Pacific, could get onto the ash pits and to the coal cranes only two or three at a time, and the inspector and I had a few heated words by telephone. The sole purpose of the speedy restoration of the engines to their trains was, it dawned on me later, to release him and a few traffic inspectors in time to get to the course before the start of the Big Race.

One day we noticed that two or three coal wagons despatched by a Yorkshire colliery had not reached us. All the wagons sent to us were invoiced in advance and usually reached Walton within a week; any odd wagon that took longer was assumed to have been held up for repairs or in a traffic delay. When a few had still not appeared after about three months investigations had to be made, eventually by the railway police. Lengthy inquiries brought to light that a coal merchant had intercepted the vehicles and altered their labels, causing them to be put in his own siding where, after stealing the coal, he had let them be shunted away, first changing the painted numbers on their sides. A court case duly followed.

A Walton driver had to give evidence at a High Court when the CLC was being sued after a train that he had worked had collided with a car on a level crossing; the accident occurred shortly after he had passed a two armed bracket signal on the approach to a facing junction. The arm for the branch had been cleared, the other, needless to say, being in its danger position; the plaintiff's counsel forced the driver to admit, however, that he had 'passed a signal at danger', which was, of course, the arm that was not intended for the train. He described to me afterwards how his evidence had proceeded; 'I kept trying to tell 'im that the arm to the right didn't apply to my train but 'e wouldn't let me explain, but there yer are – what with all them gowns and wigs they've got on, why, they've got yer beat before yer opens yer mouth!'

The LMS decided early in 1936 to close Walton as far as they were concerned and to transfer the engines, enginemen and their workings to other Liverpool depots; in July the LMS portion came to an end. The following week I was left with only 15 LNER engines and I knew that I would not be kept at Walton much longer. Oddly enough, the LMS engines came back; when the railways were nationalised in 1948 Walton found itself in the London Midland Region and was worked accordingly, the LNER engines being moved away, mostly to the Eastern Region.

The manner in which the LMS reallocated its Walton shed

staff was brutal in the extreme. The footplate staff went with their engines and did not need to change their homes but the rest of the men, nearly all elderly, were not permitted any such luck although they could readily have been accommodated at one of the other Liverpool sheds and allowed to work out their days there. The two oldest of the LMS fitters were given only a week's notice to report at Derby, the boilersmiths were sent to Manchester, and the senior clerk, a physically disabled man, was transferred to Stourton, near Leeds; all were left to find houses for themselves as best they could. Whether this was in the hope of inducing these men to find other employment, and so getting rid of them, must be left to conjecture but the second world war was only three years away; by 1940 the LMS Officers in Liverpool would have been mighty glad of all the men that they so callously sent away.

Just after Christmas 1936, I was given a brief interview by Gresley who told me that I was to fill a vacancy that he had; he did not say where but a few days later I was told to report to the Mechanical Engineer at Cowlairs as Assistant to the Works Manager.

3 In a Main Works

Cowlairs station lay about $1\frac{1}{2}$ miles to the north of Glasgow's Queen Street station and on the Glasgow to Edinburgh main line of the former North British Railway; the works was immediately alongside it. There, early in 1937, I presented myself before the Mechanical Engineer, T.E. Heywood. My new appointment was Assistant *to*, you will notice, not Assistant, and my salary increase was £15 a year or five shillings and ninepence (28p) a week. The salary that I drew was not increased by that amount, however, as I no longer received a 5 per cent Aggregation Allowance that I had had in the Running Department for irregular hours; in effect there was no increase at all.

Under Mr Heywood were the works managers at Cowlairs, Inverurie and at a few wagon works; Cowlairs had been the NBR's works and Inverurie that of the Great North of Scotland Railway; both had locomotive and carriage shops. The Cowlairs manager had three Assistants *to*, responsible for locomotives, carriages and outdoor machinery respectively; I was the Locomotive Assistant. The outdoor machinery Assistant supervised repairs to all machinery within the works and to all turntables, coaling plants, cranes, hoists and the like at stations and engine sheds all over the old NBR system.

Within the first week I had learned two somewhat depressing truths. One was that Gresley had little interest in Cowlairs and had long since concentrated all locomotive building at Doncaster and Darlington; the works had received meagre help in the way of improved machinery and facilities after the NBR Directors

39

had relinquished it to the LNER. The second was that Gresley was finding both Scottish works very handy as places of exile for men whom he had decided to despatch well out of his way, and very objectionable I found some of these individuals to be. The works offices were beggarly; Heywood and his small staff of clerks and draughtsmen, the Works Manager and his Assistants *to*, together with the works clerks and accountants, were housed in a grim stone building rather reminiscent of a converted workhouse or prison. The Manager had a tiny room of his own but his chief clerk and the three Assistants *to* had to share one office, a desk to each, this office serving as a passage for anyone who needed to visit the Manager during the day. We were told, of course, that Assistants *to* did not really need offices; our duties lay mainly in the shops, it was explained, and so our frugal facilities were of little consequence. As it was, having to do paper work, often involving calculations, in a room occupied by three others, with probably at least one telephone in use, was quite intolerable; it is elementary that any manager whose duties include interviewing men needs a private room for such purposes. The shop foremen completely lacked any proper office accommodation and made do with huts, inside their shops if they were lucky, or out of doors in the form of old coach bodies resting on bricks.

Heywood had been the Locomotive Engineer of the GNSR at Inverurie and was, I believe, of Taff Vale Railway origin. He was one of the 'old time' railway officers, being broad, heavy, with large white moustache and sporting a great gold watch chain across his ample form. He worked mainly in his office where, so his chief clerk told me, he occasionally developed spasms of rage and flung papers about the floor. When he decided on a tour of the works he went into the shops without considering for one moment that it would be courteous to send word to the Manager or the Assistants of his intentions, although he expected them to be in attendance in the course of his rounds. A bush telegraph used to operate – 'Mr Heywood is out in the works', – on receipt of which intelligence the Managers were required to cease at once whatever they were doing and to dash from shop to shop until they located the Great Man, when it then became their bounden duty to walk gracefully behind him, speaking only when spoken to. He roared his way around the workshops, ignoring his trembling Works Manager and bellowing with fearful words at every foreman and fitter that he saw; back in the offices he bawled at the clerks similarly. I soon found, however, that no one at Cowlairs was unduly put out by his violent tirades, most of the men having endured them for years; nevertheless, such behaviour belonged to the Victorian era and no one would yield to it today for a moment, and I am sure that it did not assist works progress in the slightest.

The works had an interesting history, closely connected with that of Scotland's three earliest main line railways. The first of these to appear was the Edinburgh & Glasgow, opened in February 1842, via Falkirk High; the original Edinburgh terminus was at Haymarket and most of it is still to be seen there today. Cowlairs works was built by the E&GR and was one of the earliest locomotive and carriage works in Britain; it was ready by 1842, a year before Swindon and Crewe were in operation. Two other early lines that formed the nucleus of the LNER's Scottish Area south of Aberdeen were the North British and the Edinburgh, Perth & Dundee, with works at St Margarets, in Edinburgh, and Burntisland respectively. By 1865 the three companies had amalgamated and the directors of the new company, which kept the name North British Railway, adopted Cowlairs as its main works, leaving St Margarets to be a running shed and Burntisland as a wagon factory. Various additions were made to Cowlairs shops as the NBR expanded but some of the buildings and almost certainly the main office block dated from E&GR days.

The engines that received their general repairs at Cowlairs were almost all those of NBR origin that still remained at work, together with the engines of the D11 Director, K3, J38, J39 and V1 classes that were allocated to Scottish running sheds; J38 engines were similar to the J39s but had 4ft 8in driving wheels

41

compared with the J39's 5ft 2in. The V1s were 2–6–2 three cylinder tank locomotives, mostly allocated to sheds working Glasgow suburban trains. All the NBR passenger tender engines were of 4–4–0 inside cylinder classes, except the outside cylinder Atlantic engines classified C10 and C11; the NBR never attempted to introduce six-coupled passenger tender engines, probably because of the many severe curves on its lines. All the NBR goods engines were of the 0–6–0 tender type; tank engines were mostly of 4–4–2 type for passenger work, 0–6–2 for goods and 0–6–0 for shunting.

NBR engines were extensively named, not with brass nameplates but with transfers put on in the Cowlairs paint shop. The D29 and D30 4–4–0 locomotives were dubbed after Walter Scott characters, the D34s had the names of Scottish glens, and 25 J36 goods engines that had worked in France and elsewhere overseas during the first world war were named *Ypres, Verdun, Arras,* and so on.

The works was similar to the Doncaster Plant, and to most other main railway works, possessing the usual locomotive erecting, boiler, machine and fitting shops, forge, foundry and millwrights' department, and carriage repair shops. It must have been a dreadfully congested place in NBR days as it was only half the size of Doncaster but had to cater for almost as many engines; the NBR had about 1,050 engines in its last independent years compared with the GNR's 1,350. Engines scheduled for general repairs were shunted into a reception siding and thence to the stripping shed where fitters had one of the most uncongenial tasks on the railway; they had to release and remove every member, fitting and pipe that it was possible to detach, the engines being in the filthiest state imaginable. The parts were then taken away by labourers who dropped them into a tank of boiling water and soda for the removal of the grease and the dirt which was mostly locomotive ash. The stripped engines were next taken to a repair pit in the erecting shop where the boiler and wheels were removed by the travelling cranes of which each bay had two, and at the same time the dismantled parts, each with its engine number stamped on it, were passed to the fitting shop. Within a day or two nothing was left of the engine except the frames and cylinders.

The parts went to a variety of specialist gangs; there was a gang of skilled workers who repaired the connecting and coupling rods, another that restored valve gears, and yet another that reconditioned or renewed axleboxes. Wheels, pistons, crossheads, sets of brake equipment, injectors, lubricators, regulator valves, safety valves and sandbox fittings were each dealt with by individual work parties. Boiler repairs were carried out by the boilersmiths who also renovated smokeboxes, side tanks, coal bunkers and buffer beams.

As soon as the engine frames and cylinders had been cleaned the task of repairing and reassembly was begun. First the frames and the horns that carried the axleboxes were examined and any cracks welded up, and the bolts that held the horns and the cylinders to the frames were renewed where necessary and made tight; the horns were filed true and unless the cylinders had been renewed they were rebored. Repaired parts gradually began to arrive, the fitters replacing them as they came to hand. Once the boiler was back in position, and it was seldom the previous one but another, either repaired or new, the smokebox and cab could be replaced and the cab fittings and all the piping could then be fitted. Then came the 'wheeling'; a space was cleared further along the pit, each pair of wheels was put down on the rails by the cranes, complete with its axleboxes, and the engine frame was carried by the travelling cranes to the wheels and lowered onto them, a fitter posted at each wheel guiding his axlebox into the horn as it descended. The pistons, connecting rods and valve gears could then be erected, and all the brake gear fitted.

Valve setting came next, carried out by a couple of men who did this work exclusively. All that the setting amounted to was making adjustments to ensure that both of the openings on each slide or piston valve were equal, in both fore and back gears, but this could be achieved only by trial and error, and the task called for considerable skill; steam locomotive parts are not made with

43

such precision that it is unnecessary to check the openings when the valve gears are put together and, the openings being relatively small, extreme accuracy is needed, some designs prescribing dimensions in sixty-fourths of an inch.

Thus, in the case of a slide valve engine having Stephenson's gear, if the right hand valve was found to open an inch at the front port in fore gear and only half an inch at the back the right hand fore gear eccentric rod needed lengthening by a quarter of an inch and this was done by a smith. The valve openings were measured by raising the driving wheels just clear of the rails and revolving them, usually by means of rollers and a ratchet lever. In the case of piston valves, because the setter could not see the valve heads or the ports, he had to work from marks that he had placed previously on the valve spindles. A Gresley three-cylinder engine with the rocking levers in front of the cylinders had to have the setting done in two stages; first the outside valve events had to be corrected and then the valve of the inside cylinder could be tested and corrected in turn.

New or repaired boilers, before being taken to their engines, were steamed in a shed reserved for the purpose where the safety valves were adjusted; injectors were also checked to ensure that they worked properly. As each engine was finished it was shunted into the paint shop and when its livery had been restored it was ready for return to its running shed. At one time a great deal of labour went into the painting of a locomotive and at Doncaster in the 1920s the engines were washed with pumice, all the cracks and holes in existing paintwork were filled with 'stopping', several coats of paint were applied and elaborate lining set out, all by hand, before the work was completed by an application of varnish. By the time I arrived at Cowlairs, however, drastic economies had been made; a man sprayed each engine with cheap black paint, put on the number transfers, with the name if any, and that was that.

I had two main duties in the works. One was to attend to the Outstations Department where engine components arrived from running sheds all over Scotland, and from Carlisle Canal which was included in the LNER's Scottish Area; these were usually connecting rods and valve gear parts that were cracked or broken, or had been damaged in slow speed collisions, and were beyond the scope of the shed fitters to repair. The works staff were required to repair and return them with the utmost speed, so as to get the engines to which they belonged back into traffic and I was made responsible for seeing that they did so. The parts either arrived by goods train or came in the brake compartments of passenger trains; I had to ensure that they were hustled into the fitting shop and to persuade the foreman to take them in hand promptly; frequent visits to the work benches were necessary to check that repairs were in progress, and finally I had to make certain of the return of the materials to the sheds where they were awaited. There was an Outstations Foreman who was supposed to supervise the progress of materials through the shops; my task was to urge him along and the rest of the foremen too.

My other big pursuit was known as Alterations. No designer has yet designed the perfect engine and as soon as a new type goes into service all sorts of faults develop or become apparent in time. They are usually small matters; perhaps a footstep is not in quite the right position for the drivers, a handrail ought to be a little higher, a driver's seat needs moving a few inches or some piece of the cab's equipment interferes slightly with the view along the line ahead. Then, after the engine has been in service a few months, tiresome defects begin to appear; a certain pipe repeatedly breaks because it needs stronger fastenings, or the drain cock operating rod fractures because some other part chafes it and the gear needs a better layout. Such discoveries were usually reported by the LRSs, with suggestions for improvement, and when the CME had decided how corrections had best be made he notified his MEs and they, in turn, instructed the works managers to make the necessary changes as the engines became due for general repairs.

All so simple, it might be thought, that such minor matters ought to take their course quite readily, but not when, as in the case of Gresley's J39 0–6–0 engines, there were over *200* changes to be made to one class alone. Moreover, there were about seven types of J39, and modifications required on some were found to be incorporated in those built later; as each engine entered the works for overhaul an inspection was needed to ascertain whether some of the reforms had already been made, perhaps in another works. The LRSs were not always consistent; an adjustment requested in Scotland did not necessarily suit the people in the NE Area. Anyway, I was required to follow up the Alterations and to see that they were made, and as the main aim of the erecting shop was to get the engines repaired quickly the inclusion of all the modifications ordered was often a near impossibility. I am sure that many were never carried out at all.

There was very little scientific management at Cowlairs as there would be in a works today; the organisation had not changed very much since the mid 19th Century. The erecting shop was dreadfully untidy, the engines being surrounded by a litter of boiler tubes, chimneys, smokebox doors, superheater elements and copper pipes. Now and then I was instructed to get the floor and benches tidied; the difficulty always was that many of the oddments had been lying around for months or years and no one quite knew whether they belonged to engines in the shop or whether they lay discarded because new parts had long since replaced them. A shed was needed where each engine's components could be laid out in stalls bearing the engine's number, ready to be taken to the shop when the erectors were ready for them, but Cowlairs works just did not have the spare accommodation for such a scheme.

I managed to effect small improvements here and there. A weakness in the Doncaster Crimpsall that I recollected was the time we wasted looking for nuts and bolts; when the engines were stripped many of the nuts and bolts became damaged or destroyed in the process. The erecting shop fitters never seemed to have sufficient and their foremen allowed only limited quantities of new nuts and bolts to be drawn from the stores, on the principle that if the fitter wasn't given any he would find them somehow, somewhere for himself.

As in the Crimpsall, the Cowlairs erecting shop floor was permanently littered with nuts, some in fair condition, some too damaged for use, and I accordingly had a small bench put up, selected a man who was confined to light work and gave him the duty of picking up all the nuts and bolts that he could find, reconditioning those that were repairable with taps, stocks and dies and putting what he salvaged into boxes where the fitters could get them; the unusable ones he conveyed to a scrap bin so that men did not waste time examining them. After a month or so of this I was called to task by the works accountants because I hadn't computed the saving that my little stroke of policy had produced; I was required to show in pounds, shillings and pence that the man's work justified his wages. To me the saving seemed obvious but I made up a few figures and presented them to the book keepers who accepted that sound economies had been effected. It was my first attempt at reform but the erecting shop foreman taught me a lesson as a result; I had not, he said, been sufficiently sharp to ensure that the higher management appreciated what I had done. 'Whatever ye do, lad', he said, 'see that you get credit for it!' In other words, forget the silly schoolboy principle that it is bad form to show off; showmanship, artfully applied, can be the key to success.

I had few opportunities to talk to the men; fitters on piecework do not as a rule have much spare time for conversation. The foremen, however, all had repertoires of railway anecdotes, and one or two could remember the working of trains up the 2,090yd incline from Queen Street station to Cowlairs by rope and fixed engine, a method of assistance to trains that was not discontinued until 1909. The incline has gradients varying from 1 in 50 to 1 in $41\frac{1}{2}$, and its lower part is through a 997yd tunnel; the endless rope, of steel, was 2.78 miles long and lay along the four foot way of both tracks.

Trains descended from Cowlairs without a locomotive in front but with two or three 15-ton four-wheeled brake vehicles at the leading end instead, each manned by a brakesman who controlled the carriages down the incline and halted them at the station. Every engine that worked from Queen Street had a second drawhook on its front buffer beam, fitted with its hook downwards; a messenger chain put onto the inverted hook attached the engine to the steel rope. The order to the man in charge of the large fixed steam engine at Cowlairs to start the train was given through the signalmen, and every train that left invariably took two or three brake vehicles with it, attached to the rear. When the train reached Cowlairs, doing so in about four minutes, the Cowlairs engineman shut off steam, allowing the rope to slacken and the messenger chain to drop off the inverted hook.

On 24 January 1902 the inevitable accident happened; the 9.10am passenger train from Queen Street had just stopped out of course at Cowlairs when two brake vehicles which it had hauled up the incline and had been unshipped a few moments before, ran into its rear. The Cowlairs engineman had begun to replenish several oil cups when the train was half way up the incline, instead of watching his controls, and did not stop the fixed engine soon enough; as a result the messenger chain, failing to fall clear before the locomotive reached the steel rope's main pulley wheel, dislodged some boards that nearly derailed the carriages. The train was scheduled to pass Cowlairs without stopping and, anticipating this, the brakesman had 'slipped' his brake vehicles by knocking out a pin. The method of operation, which had been in force for about 60 years, was remarkably crude; the Cowlairs engine house controls had an indicator dial with a pointer that went round it once for every hundred revolutions of the engine's crankshaft, and the engineman's normal practice was to shut off steam at 98 revolutions for a light train or 104 for one that was heavy. There was no equipment of any kind to guard against overwinding. The large and rather classical stone building that used to house the fixed engine was still, in 1937, to be seen alongside Cowlairs station.

One of the LNER's Glasgow suburban stations was Milngavie and in the late 1930s a remarkable edifice stood there in the form of a length of track to support the Bennie Railplane, a suspended monorail system. It was to have cars with torpedo shaped ends fitted with air propellers; the track was a continuous lattice box girder supported by trestles 80ft apart and carrying two rails for Up and Down 'trains' respectively. It was intended that the air propellers on each car would be driven by oil engines, or by electric motors, and great possibilities in the way of speed were anticipated. In 1930 a 430ft experimental stretch of monorail track, with a car fitted up internally in Pullman style, was built at Milngavie by arrangement over an LNER track, to demonstrate that the equipment could be laid readily along any existing railway route without interfering with the ordinary rail traffic; it never appears to have been specified how tunnels were to be bypassed. I believe trials of some sort were attempted but by 1937 all but the patent seemed to have been abandoned; the forlorn equipment stood at Milngavie for a few more years and was then quietly dismantled.

Towards the end of 1937 I was offered another running shed post in the Southern Area which I accepted; Cowlairs, I am afraid, was the one place on the railway that I failed to find particularly accordant. There was an unpleasant and uneasy feeling among the works personnel all the time I was there; whether the bombastic Heywood generated it or whether it seemed that the works was out of Gresley's favour I do not know; I do know, however, that, shortly after I left, the works manager was moved away, and that a little later his successor went similarly.

4 Engine Sheds – East Anglia and North East

My new depot was at Lowestoft, on the former Great Eastern Railway and where passenger traffic, very heavy in summer, prevailed on three main lines leading to London, Norwich and Yarmouth. The LNER predominated in the town, being the biggest employer of labour and owning a harbour almost three miles in length, a sea lock, swing bridges, and the South Pier which the Town Council used for a peppercorn rent for seaside amusements. The company also possessed a works for harbour maintenance, a dry dock, slipways and a 13 acre sleeper creosoting and storage depot. The Council eyed these possessions with jealous envy and made petty attacks on the LNER at Town Hall meetings; when the Mayor was on the Bench as Chairman things went hard for any LNER man guilty when cycling of some trivial traffic offence.

The Norwich line included part of East Anglia's earliest railway, the Yarmouth & Norwich opened in May 1844, with George Stephenson its first chairman and his son Robert its engineer; the original Norwich station still stands, in Riverside. A year later the Norwich & Brandon Railway opened, the two companies amalgamating to form the Norfolk Railway; the present Norwich motive power depot includes buildings that were once the NR's workshops. So that the N&BR could enter the Riverside terminal the company's civil engineer, G.P. Bidder, designed a swing bridge to span the navigable River Wensum; the Government's Inspector General of Railways examined and approved it on 8 December 1845, his illustrated

Above: The Elsecar pumping engine, near Barnsley, the only Newcomen engine still occupying its original site. *Below:* A typical colliery winding engine; Markham Main colliery, near Chesterfield. (*National Coal Board*).

Above: Chester running shed, CLC. (*Real Photographs Co Ltd*). *Below:* Brunswick running shed, Liverpool, CLC.

Report, still preserved, describing it in detail. It was the first railway swing bridge in the world and lasted until replaced in 1905.

The line from Lowestoft towards Norwich was the result of prodigious efforts by Sir Samuel Morton Peto who did much to develop the town. Born in 1809, he was first a partner in a firm that built many London edifices, including the Houses of Parliament and Nelson's Column; then he turned to railway contracts and built the Y&NR. Realising that Lowestoft could be made into an excellent port he promoted the Lowestoft Railway & Harbour Company, his line being joined in 1847 to the Y&NR, or NR as it had become, at Reedham; then he constructed the South Pier and the first of the outer harbours, the Marine Parade and many of its houses. In 1843 he bought and rebuilt Somerleyton Hall, near Lowestoft, living there until 1862; he was knighted for Crimean War services at Balaklava where he and a partner laid 39 miles of military railway, shipping the materials and workmen from Britain. The reputation that he left was excellent; the Inspector General of Railways, Major General C.W. Pasley, reporting on the N&BR, said that:

> The gentlemen who accompanied me on this inspection having mentioned the very orderly conduct and good behaviour of the railway workmen, who had committed no excesses in the country, either by personal ill-usage or depredations on property, I was happy to hear this favourable report afterwards confirmed by a Norfolk gentleman not connected with the railway . . . I ascribe this in a great measure to the just and kind treatment of these men by Mr Peto, who pays them their full wages regularly every week, disdaining the truck system, by which the employers of workmen too often keep them in arrears, and extort an improper profit out of their wages which renders them discontented, and prone to riot and irregularities.

Most GER depots, Lowestoft included, were wretchedly furnished in the way of equipment. The shed had four dead-end tracks which, with a few outside sidings, afforded just enough accommodation for all the engines at night. There was no hoist for raising engines nor any power driven tools, and two or three caverns beneath a 50,000gal water tank represented the workshop, store and messing facilities. Instead of expending on plant, tools and buildings, the GER ran its engines by ruthless coercion; men were expected to get results without the help of materials or appliances, and so were their foremen. There were no fixed hours of duty for foremen and other supervisors, and hopes of advancement held by most such men gave the management a permanent dagger that could be held at the throat of anyone showing even slight restlessness; he merely had to be told that there were signs of his inability to meet the simple requirements of his post, with his promotion prospects becoming uncertain.

Supervisors throughout Norfolk and Suffolk seemed to have been branded by rigorous GER management; small incidents left them shaking in terror of being denounced. They kept alert continuously lest censure seemed to be coming their way, ready if it did to divert it onto someone else, which led to battles of wits and bad feeling between departments. Rural stationmasters, on reporting minor derailments, would plead that the despatch of the breakdown train be avoided and that the barest items of rerailing equipment be sent by light engine or by a convenient train, as if the arrival of a breakdown train stained their record. If an engine ran off the rails the driver was left to apply to me for help; the stationmaster just ignored him.

My Lowestoft men were first class; the drivers were masters of their calling and the fitters were excellent, having valuable knowledge of the Westinghouse brake, with which most of my engines were equipped. The passenger engines, all tank locomotives, were 2–4–2s, F3s for the main line trains and F4s for the Waveney Valley line which, on account of several small timber bridges, had severe axle load restrictions, although it could also be worked by E4 2–4–0s, the tender version of the F3, but had less weight on the driving wheels. The goods engines were J15 0–6–0s; they were splendid little locomotives which, with light axle loadings, could work anywhere. For shunting I had J67 0–6–0 tank locomotives. All these engines, of GER design and with vacuum equipment for coaching stock as well as the Westinghouse brake, were very reliable; indeed, I soon learned that GE engines were well built and seldom broke down. Having a crosshead that worked on a single slide bar, for example, the troubles that result from multiple slide bar systems were avoided. The Westinghouse equipment on locomotives was usually quite trouble free, provided that the air reservoirs were frequently drained of the water that the steam pumps squeezed out of the air as they compressed it; the pumps could stick and fail to start if routine maintenance was neglected but my fitters took care to keep them in good order.

A Stratford J39 engine arrived daily at Lowestoft from Goodmayes and worked the 3.50pm goods train back. With a tractive effort of 25,664 lb, the J39s, described when they appeared in 1926 as general service locomotives, were powerful, but most of them ran in dreadful condition and as we seldom received the same engines two days together my day shift fitters spent most of their time repairing them. Loss of a big end cotter on the way to Lowestoft was a common occurrence, often allowing the whole big end to work loose, which might well involve taking down the connecting rod and fitting new brasses; another frequent incident was the loss of the nut from a small-end gudgeon pin, which allowed the pin to slide out of place until it struck some fixed part, bending the connecting rod, displacing the slide bars and generally smashing up the gear between the frames. The inside-cylinder design was unsuitable for such big engines, the forces developed when the massive parts were moving at speed being too much for the fastenings; unfortunately the LNER had 289 J39s in all and we had to endure and do our best with them but they were one of Gresley's less happy creations.

Water supplies are limited in the Eastern Counties; lacking the vast moorland reservoirs that feed the central and north country towns so adequately, the water sources are rivers, deep wells and boreholes. Supplies for my engines had to come from the town mains and out of a pool that collected water from gulleys through a cutting. The water from both sources was very hard and produced so much scale that the boilers had to be washed out every six working days, and needed 'sifting' every six months when about half the scale-coated flue tubes were renewed, the remainder being changed six months later. The injector cones furred up rapidly and needed monthly cleaning in weak acid solution, and so did the clacks which, on GER engines, were on the boiler side and easily accessible; on a GCR engine which I had for a few months, the injectors were on the firebox faceplate, with internal delivery pipes from which the water flowed somewhere beneath the steam dome. Scale blocked and almost closed the ends of these pipes, and our only remedy was to take out the heavy regulator valve and saw a few inches off the pipe, hoping that the injectors would then work until the engine was called in for a works overhaul.

Water softening was introduced at Lowestoft by the CME who hoped to reduce the water's 15° of hardness, which means 15 grains of dissolved impurity per gallon, to 3° and so eliminate scaling. A 'milk' or emulsion of lime and soda that the softening plant put into the water turned the impurities into a precipitate that settled and could be drawn off, but it left soluble salts behind that caused heavy priming.

No one quite knows what goes on in a locomotive boiler when steam generates but under certain conditions the steam will gather some of the water and carry it to the cylinders; this is called priming. Hot water will not apply power to a piston and priming, if it goes on, will empty a boiler in no time. With such a handicap my drivers just could not work their trains and the CME reduced the softening, leaving our water about 6° hard; this lessened the priming but rendered the whole softening process rather pointless. I wonder whether the CME ever realised that our engines took at least half their water at Reedham, Beccles and other places where softening was not applied?

I soon developed the greatest admiration for the Lowestoft

fishermen who went out aboard their drifters and trawlers in all seasons of the year and in all weathers. Most people know only the seaside's summer aspects; spend a winter in a place like Lowestoft and you then come to appreciate what *cold* weather can really be like, and to realise that tales of the sea freezing on men's hands as the nets are hauled up are really true. Stormy seas with gigantic waves, biting winds and icy rain; those are the usual working conditions of the skippers and their crews, men for whom I came to have the highest regard, and more when on the outbreak of World War II they served in the Navy with their vessels converted into minesweepers, clearing the deadly German mines from the shipping channels.

In May 1939 I witnessed, unfortunately, a fatal accident; a few D2 tender engines had recently arrived at Yarmouth Beach depot on the Midland & Great Northern line and one of them came to my shed for water. The young fireman hauled the water column's heavy leather hose up onto the tender but while it was still filling the tank he lost his balance and fell head first. The Ministry of Transport sent an Inspector, Mr J.A. Sinclair, to hold an Inquiry; a few months earlier he had filled a vacancy at the Ministry for which I had applied without success. I envied him but had I known it I needed only patience; 14 years later, and with far more experience, I was to obtain the next similar post that fell vacant and, moreover, to have Mr Sinclair under my supervision.

World War II started for the British on 3 September 1939 and we had to fit every engine with tarpaulin screens immediately, to render fire glare invisible from above. It was grimly realised that ours was the nearest British locomotive depot to Germany; our first enemies were, however, the 'blackout' and the 1939/40 winter. Two blackout incidents occurred that would have been fatal but for Providence; one was to a storesman who, attempting at night to cycle home along the completely unlit harbour quay, which was his authorised route, rode his bicycle over the edge. Fortunately his 12ft fall was into water and not into a boat, and his cries for help soon brought others who pulled him out. The other lucky man was also cycling home along the same route at night when a strong wind prevented him from hearing a challenge by a Naval sentry who fired, the bullet missing the man's head by inches. At a meeting next day the LNER Harbour Master persuaded the Naval authorities to be more reasonable.

The winter was a severe test; the locomotive water columns, the water softening plant and even the pipes from the locomotive tanks to the boiler injectors froze up, the blackout restrictions having to be bypassed and fires and flares kept going in order to maintain the running of the railway. Even the coal froze into a solid mass in the wagons. Somehow the fitting staff managed to carry on with their duties despite the terrible cold.

A few ludicrous 'precautions' were put in hand early in 1940. I was required by high level orders to cover the 50,000gal water tank 'so that it wouldn't be seen from the air' and was given coils of old signal wire and scrap wagon sheets for the purpose. My labourers stretched the wires across the tank and then spread the heavy sheets over them, or tried to, working all the time above nine feet of icy water; within a few weeks most of the wires had broken and all the sheets had fallen into the tank. Meanwhile the Army was at work camouflaging St John's Church near the harbour entrance; the troops hung long canvas lengths down the sides of a gigantic scaffold that they had built around the tower and spire. The camouflage remained intact for about a week and then the canvas lengths were ripped loose by the spring gales and they flew from the scaffold like monstrous streamers until within a few days the wind carried them into the sea; the scaffold remained until the steel rusted away and the poles fell down of their own accord. I can hardly believe that the disguise, while it lasted, caused any Germans the least apprehension.

Hitherto confined to local trains, Lowestoft men were soon taking trains as far as Ely and Cambridge. A Lowestoft concert hall became HMS *Europa* and served throughout the War as a drafting centre for thousands of sailors who travelled to and from the town in special trains; at times we were providing engines for two or three 12 coach Naval specials a week, most of which went to the Clyde. Later in the War we worked trainloads of cement for aerodrome construction and after that trains of open 16 ton wagons full of bombs. Lowestoft never had a big concentrated air raid but, in all, the town had 2,047 air raid warnings, and air attacks cost 192 civilians their lives; 630 high explosive bombs were dropped on the town, parts of which were severely damaged. Throughout all this the Lowestoft railwaymen performed their duties magnificently; only once, and I repeat once, was the scheduled departure of an engine from Lowestoft shed delayed due to an air raid, apart from occasions when bomb damage temporarily prevented any movements, or unexploded bombs blocked the tracks. Indeed, we became accustomed to the warnings and took little notice of them until Naval guns went into action and enemy aircraft were actually in sight or, at night, we knew them to be overhead.

When Dunkirk fell in June 1940 the possibilities of invasion attempts along the eastern and southern coasts were regarded as very real and one evening I was called out to supervise the disablement of every workable locomotive by the removal of vital parts such as injector cones which were hidden until next morning. The following evening we had to send every engine to Reedham, except those incapable of movement, bringing them back at daybreak, one of the fitters going with them and doing what repairs he could in the sidings; this nightly evacuation of engines went on for several months and we also had our breakdown train taken away for storage inland.

In 1942 shed foremen were re-designated Locomotive Shed Masters, but in June 1944 I was a foreman once more when I became Mechanical Foreman at Gateshead. Every large LNER engine shed had a mechanical foreman working immediately under the shed master and responsible for supervising his fitting staff and the general maintenance of his engines. By 1944 I had served 12 years in the Running Department, learning a good deal about LNER engines in service; very soon I was to learn much more.

Gateshead depot, on the south bank of the Tyne and opposite Newcastle-upon-Tyne station, was one of four principal depots providing engines for the East Coast main line; it was quite outdated, having been planned for locomotives of the 1850s. The main shed, of roundhouse design, was a huge rectangular building that covered four turntables, all of which were crossed in succession by a single access track. There were about 18 bays to each table but many were too short except for very small engines, of which the depot had only a few, or wagons, and usually stood empty although the running foremen were always short of stabling places. Whether roundhouses are better than sheds containing through or dead-end parallel tracks is something for debate. An engine can be run from a roundhouse stall and turned to face the required way quickly and in one operation, and by merely going to the turntable the foreman can see at once all the engines in its stalls at a glance. An engine in a roundhouse stall is in far less danger of inadvertent movement when fitters are at work on it than in a straight shed. But if by some accident an engine tumbles into the turntable pit every engine in the stalls becomes stranded there. To draw an engine not in steam out of a stall the opposite stall must be empty and two other engines are needed, one to pull the dead engine onto the turntable and the other to shunt it away. There was also a straight shed at Gateshead for the Pacifics; they were too long for the roundhouse stalls.

The depot lay alongside buildings that had once housed the Gateshead Works opened by the York, Newcastle & Berwick Railway formed in 1847 by the amalgamation of several small concerns, and closed in 1932 when Gresley made Darlington the main works of the NE area. The overhead cranes were maintained, however, enabling the Running Department to take the erecting shop into use during the War for periodical examinations.

Gateshead had about 130 passenger and mixed traffic engines, mostly A1, A2 and A3 Pacifics, and Classes V2, D49, B16 and C7. There were a few goods and shunting engines but almost all the goods engines for the lines south of the Tyne were based at Borough Gardens or Tyne Dock. Gateshead engines went anywhere between King's Cross and Edinburgh, and to Carlisle, running prodigious mileages; shortly after nationalisation in 1948 Col Rudgard, the Chief Motive Power Officer of British Railways and a late LMS man, visited the depot and was astonished and not a little mortified to discover that its engines were working greater weekly mileages than any of those at depots along the West Coast main line.

My duty was to keep these Gateshead engines in running order and by the first week I had appreciated that I had no easy mission. After a month I found it to be a gruelling struggle like that of the unfortunate Sisyphus who was condemned for ever to roll uphill a great rock that always toppled back again. The engines were mostly in a shocking state; they arrived at the shed with bent connecting rods, dreadful steam leakages and defective vacuum brakes, but the demand for motive power was so pressing because of the huge movements of troops, sailors and airmen, munitions, stores and German prisoners that there simply wasn't time to get the repairs done. The running foremen's policy as each engine arrived was that 'it got here so I can use it for another train' and away it would go within the hour. Only if an engine collapsed completely was I told that it was 'stopped' when it was then a case of all hands to its rescue to get it back to work again.

The mechanical foreman's position was difficult. His primary duty was to keep the engines at work but if, when hauling a train, an engine broke down he was called upon to explain why it had failed. So whenever at a shed an engine was obviously in need of attention he could take it out of traffic, and was then expected to repair it with the speed of magic, with the District Officer's extreme disfavour upon him all the time it was detained; alternatively he could let the engine take its chance and hope it would manage to reach another depot before it expired.

The North Eastern shed masters and officers were remarkably unlike those I knew in the Southern Area; many were lazy and idle, leaving the work to their foremen and looking on with self satisfaction. The NER had been a prosperous railway, generously provided with staff, and its managers had had little need to exert themselves, a state of mind that continued into LNER days. NER clerical staff performed an eight hour day that *included* $1\frac{1}{2}$ hours for lunch; having carried this licence into the LNER era they had no intention of relinquishing it, even when the War was at its height. The principal locomotive officers seldom visited Gateshead, having no desire, it seemed, to hear any of my current difficulties; while British and Allied troops, battling in Northern France, were in need of all the reinforcements and supplies that transport could provide, these men played billiards in the basement of the railway hotel, and their clerks resolutely worked $6\frac{1}{2}$ hours day by day.

In the main my fitting staff did what they could to keep the engines in something like proper condition, and the drivers managed to work the engines as they found them, but a reactionary outlook had developed. A long and humiliating period of wretched unemployment on the cold Northumberland and Durham coasts had lasted until 1940, children in homes inadequately heated had been short of food and deficiently clothed, all at a time when in London and the south the affluent 'dividend drawing classes' were filling the restaurants and theatres and did not want to know what was happening amongst the barbarians of the north – barbarians who, incidentally, had invented the railways that the people of the south had copied. Is it surprising that when Tynesiders suddenly found that their labour was desperately needed some of them sought revenge, as they did, on managers and employers?

My whole repair organisation was continually undermined by wanton thefts of brass and copper parts from the engines. Some of the robberies were, I fear, committed by staff delinquents but street drifters and spivs who sneaked into the premises were mostly responsible. Copper pipes disappeared from engines about to work their trains, leaving them disabled until new pipes could be made and fitted, valves, handles, covers and other brass parts vanished from engine cabs, and big end brasses took flight from fitters' benches during the mealbreaks. The materials were, of course, conveyed to receivers who ruthlessly sabotaged the railways and the war effort by handling stolen metal; no one seemed to know where these fences performed their despicable trade but I could cheerfully have sought them out with a gun and shot them dead on the spot.

The defective designs found on most Gresley engines provided another handicap; Gresley's locomotives were capable of both speed and hard work, and the V2s 'won the War', at least on the East Coast, but they bristled with faults. Had Gresley been less of an autocrat, instead of defending his designs and leaving the shed people to run the engines as best they might, some of the failings might have been eliminated. The 2 to 1 valve gear for three-cylinder engines is well known; because of slack in the pin joints, the middle valve's own weight caused excessive port openings when the valve reciprocated at speed, allowing the middle piston to receive more than its one third share of steam and making the middle connecting rod perform an excess of work. If this overheated the middle big end and the driver remained unaware of it the bearing's white metal would melt, followed by the disintegration of the brasses which would allow the piston to smash the cylinder cover and itself as well, and perhaps bend the connecting rod. An engine crippled by such a calamity was towed into Gateshead depot usually about once a fortnight, the repairs occupying many days.

Various but vain efforts were made to design a middle connecting rod that would resist overheating and a Gateshead A3 engine was fitted with an experimental rod of some wonderful new pattern, on which I had to report. Every month I testified that the engine had worked without complaint about its middle rod, until one day it was inspected in Darlington works for some purpose; alas, the experimental rod had vanished and in its place was one of ordinary design. Someone, in an unknown shed, had previously removed the fancy rod which was never seen again; I forget how I explained my favourable reports on a non existent rod but it was difficult!

To describe Gresley's slide bar design as faulty would be an understatement. When an engine with driving wheels behind its cylinders is running forwards its crossheads, whichever way they are moving, press upwards; thus on engines with crossheads between upper and lower bars the upper bars need very firm anchorage. The British Railways Britannia engines had an ideal arrangement, each upper bar being attached centrally beneath an inverted base that took all the upward thrusts. But the front ends of Gresley's upper bars were *bolted* down, with the nuts uppermost, and these bolts and nuts simply could not withstand the pounding that they received and were perpetually stretching and coming loose; shed fitters were continually screwing them up, with additional washers to make the split pins bear against the upper faces of the nuts. Gresley knew all about this, and occasionally his technical assistants went to the sheds and checked on bar fastenings; as these men always gave advance notice of and the reasons for their visits, Running Superintendents, conscious of possible charges of neglect, took good care that all loose slide bars were thoroughly tightened before the investigators arrived.

The 'Britannia' method of mounting slide bars was apparently introduced into Britain by R.E.L. Maunsell, CME from 1913 to 1937 of the SE&CR and then the SR; he applied it to certain SR engines after, I feel certain, he had noticed a similar arrangement on an Irish 4–4–0 inside cylinder engine of the Celtic class when he was CME of the GS&WR. The Celtics, six in number, were built at Broadstone by the Midland Great Western; a drawing in the September 1902 issue of the *Locomotive Magazine* depicts their slide bar arrangement very clearly.

Gresley's 'balanced' regulator valve, having two valves fitted so that the steam pushed one open and held the other shut, was perfect in theory but not in practice. The design, applied in the 1840s and fairly satisfactory with low steam pressures, required the two valves to be *exactly* the same distance apart as their seats, which was impossible as, however skilfully made, the two valves could not rest on their seats with *absolute* equality; one was always a *little* lighter on its seat than the other, letting steam leak through. The leaks soon wore grooves in the valve seat and so worsened, the steam filling the superheater and the steam chest; in such circumstances an unattended engine left improperly secured could move away on its own, and this once happened at Gateshead when a V2 engine started off, ran slowly for about 200yd into the straight shed and struck another engine, causing much damage.

Providing that they were properly stabled with the cylinder cocks open and in mid-gear these engines were generally safe, except that clouds of steam poured unceasingly from the drain cock pipes; more than one man has fallen headlong into an engine pit when groping through such vapour which would be all the denser on frosty days. On 13 March 1954 a leaking regulator indirectly caused a fatality; after a V2 engine's coupling rod came adrift between Thirsk and York, fitters sent to make the locomotive moveable began to dismantle the rods and valve gears but when one of them prised the righthand piston forward with a bar the combination lever shifted the valve, opening the front port. Steam filled the cylinder; its pressure was low but it jerked the piston back so violently that the man with the bar was killed.

Gresley's tenders had handbrakes that were most unreliable. There was a hand screw for the brake and another for the water scoop; the handbrake screw acted on a heavy cross shaft that, turning in bearings on the tender frames, operated the brake blocks. The scoop screw's shaft did not have bearings but was designed as a sleeve that revolved around the handbrake shaft; all very nice on a drawing but Gresley forgot about *rust* and that water scoops sometimes go unused for long periods. These sleeves frequently became rustbound on the brake shafts, causing the handbrake screws, when applied, to tighten against the scoop gear instead of pulling the brake rods, and many an engine with this defect has been left unsecured by enginemen who believed that they had applied the brake properly.

Most big LNER engines had two mechanical lubricators mounted on the running plates above the wheels; they were oil containers with pumps that forced the oil through small bore copper pipes, one lubricator supplying the axleboxes and the other the cylinders and piston valve sleeves; one of the engine's moving parts worked them so that the oil consumption was proportionate to the distance travelled. For axleboxes the arrangement was ideal, as long as the supply pipes remained intact and that the somewhat vulnerable ratchet working the pumps did not go wrong. It was less effective for the cylinders and steam chests as the pumps had to force the oil against steam pressure, relying on tiny spring loaded ball valves to prevent the steam from pushing the oil back. The valves were not very effective because if the balls did not seat properly steam soon blew all the oil out of the lubricators and onto the running plates where it lay in great sticky pools. The displacement lubricator is far better for oiling a locomotive's 'front end'; each feed has a control with which the enginemen can regulate the oil flow, and a little window that enables the delivery rate to be observed. There are no mechanical parts to wear or break down.

The larger Gresley engines also had grease lubrication for the valve gear pins and bearings, and for most shafts and trunnions; the grease nipples needed replenishment by hand screwed grease guns and two women on my staff, known as the 'Grease Queens', were allocated exclusively to this work. These ladies, I discovered, had no idea how many nipples they had to grease on each engine; they greased those that they saw and that was that. Nor did anyone else at Gateshead know either, or have much notion of where they were located. The need to provide shed staff with details of the grease nipple locations had never been thought of and when I revealed this the Darlington drawing office staff, to cover their shame, hurriedly produced diagrams of the engines, depicting the nipples, and distributed them at once. I believe there were 47 on an A4 engine; a few were in quite inaccessible places and never received any grease at all!

Gresley's tender water gauges were vertical tubes with small holes along them every few inches. Water filled the tube to the tender tank's level when a quarter turn of the tube opened a valve, giving the driver a rough but sufficient indication of how much water there was. But the tube did not reach down into the tender's 1,000gal well and when water ceased to run from the tube a driver had no means of knowing whether there were 1,000 gallons still in hand or his tender was empty. Drivers thus regarded empty tubes as empty tenders, and the wells carried 1,000 gallons of water that were never used.

In 1945 I became a shed master once more, this time at Melton Constable on the Midland & Great Northern Joint Railway, years ago a splendid line, according to some books, but drifting into a sad and dismal state by the time I reached it. Schoolboys knew it as the 'Muddle & Get Nowhere Railway' and others implied that it was a 'kept' railway under masters at Doncaster and Derby by referring to it as 'Managed & Governed from the North'. It amounted to a straggling 'main' line from Great Yarmouth through Melton Constable and South Lynn to Peterborough, with another line bearing westwards from it at Sutton Bridge to join the former Midland Railway's route via Saxby to Leicester. From Melton there was a branch to Norwich and another to Cromer; the Cromer to North Walsham and Yarmouth to Lowestoft coastal routes were known as the Norfolk & Suffolk Joint Lines, being owned jointly by the M&GNR and the LNER.

Since 1883 the system had functioned as the Eastern & Midlands Railway, being taken over jointly by the MR and GNR in 1893 and allowed to run as a separate concern with its own rolling stock. MR and GNR hopes that with the line's aid they could develop the East Anglian coast resorts soon faded and the two owning companies, which in 1923 became the LMS and the LNER, let the M&GN continue as they had found it, spending no more than absolutely necessary on annual maintenance, as little as they could on wages and salaries and nothing at all on improvements. By 1936 the LMS had lost interest in the line and decided that they had seen enough of it, telling the LNER directors to run it on their own. Before long it had become the LNER's comic turn.

Melton Constable, 41½ miles from Yarmouth and 32 from South Lynn, was a railway village named after Melton Hall nearby; The E&MR turned it from a hamlet into a miniature Swindon or Crewe by building a small works, a three track dead-end engine shed and a few rows of houses. In the 17th or 18th Century the family at the Hall became connected by a marriage with the stately people who occupied Seaton Delaval in Northumberland, a great house that is now largely a ruin; an inn built at Seaton Sluice on the A193 road was named 'The Melton Constable' and is still there.

My depot had about 35 engines which worked all four routes, going westwards as far as South Lynn and occasionally beyond; the shed lay on the southern side of the station's single island platform. There was also a tiny platform with a small waiting room supposed to be set apart for a certain local worthy whose family had, it seems, assisted the railway's construction by giving land or selling it very cheaply, reserving certain rights in return. The works had been closed since 1937.

The engines were D16s for the passenger trains, 0–6–0s of both M&GN and GER origin for goods and two or three shunting engines. There were ex GCR D9s at South Lynn, and Yarmouth Beach had its D1 and D2 ex GNR engines, once the pride of the East Coast main line but relegated to the M&GN because no one elsewhere wanted them. There were proper sets of engine diagrams but the amateurish M&GN traffic staff could barely understand them and shifted the engines from train to train as they pleased; other depots' engines consequently became mixed up with my own.

Track layouts at Melton were very inadequate; there were no sidings beyond the platform ends from which engines could set back onto their trains, although the Board of Trade had recommended them in E&MR days, and they had to stand on the main line. The Cromer line was double from Melton to Brinington level crossing a mile away but it might as well have

Above: Walton-on-the-Hill running shed, Liverpool, CLC. *Below:* Walton-on-the-Hill; the shed yard on Grand National day, with LNER Pacific No 2547 on the ashpit.

Above: Lowestoft running shed, LNER. *Below:* Among the various loco-
motive types at Lowestoft shed in the author's care were several types of
GER 2–4–2 tank used on branch and local services. This is one of the Class
F3 type. (*L&GRP 13567*).

been single; the clumsy arrangement at the station's west end prevented Cromer trains from leaving the Down platform, from where they usually departed, if a train from Brinington was approaching. Most of the M&GN signalling sufficed for such a railway but there were several places where siding outlet signals were not interlocked with the trap points but were irregularly coupled with them so that both worked together; it should not have been possible to clear the signal until the points had first been closed.

Melton had two groups of up sidings, entered in opposite directions, which lured shunters into attempting dangerous fly shunting when taking wagons from group to group; the down sidings were similarly arranged. Fly shunting means drawing a wagon towards a set of facing points, releasing the engine from the vehicle while both are in motion, letting the engine run ahead and then reversing the points so that the wagon overtakes the engine on a parallel track; the engine can then get behind the wagon and push it into place. I forecast to the stationmaster that his fly shunting would soon result in an accident, and it happened; one day a small ex M&GN 0–6–0 tank engine did not get far enough ahead and the wagon collided with one of the outside cylinders, smashing it off the engine frame. The handy little engine became scrap as the special casting of a new cylinder was not worth while.

Most M&GN track was on pebble ballast which the trains squeezed from between the sleepers as they passed, about the most unsuitable material that could have been chosen, except mire. The single line stretches were worked by the electric token system, most of the token stations being three or four miles apart; Even though automatic token exchange apparatus was fitted to M&GN engines reduced speeds were necessary at all the passing places as the parent companies had never attempted to improve them by straightening one side and signalling it for either way running, as the Northern Counties Committee in Ireland had done to accelerate the traffic. Much of the land occupied by the M&GN tracks had been given or sold at nominal prices by the landowners to help the promotion of the line; not unnaturally they parted with as little as possible and the railway fences were thus pretty near the track formation. The farmers grew their cereals as close to the fences as they could, particularly barley, and when it ripened waited hopefully for a locomotive spark to start a fire. It was much easier to collect compensation from the M&GNR for lost crops than to mow the corn and cart it to the barns; there were some very serious cornfield fires during my period at Melton that cost the railway heavy sums.

As well as the engine shed I had the water supply and a gas plant to supervise, and two little engine sheds, at Norwich and Cromer, each with a driver in immediate charge. The water was from two boreholes; it was hard but absolutely pure and drinkable. Normally it lay about 400ft down but during the War the RAF sunk a borehole a few miles away, dropping our water level to about 700ft; that's how short of ready water we were in Norfolk.

Having no knowledge of gas production beyond that acquired at a few University lectures I had to do some study. The plant produced coal gas for the station and the railway houses in the village, very few having electricity, and oil gas for the ancient carriages; it was obvious that these vehicles, lettered M&GN for accountancy purposes, would end their days on the Joint Line and would never receive electric lighting equipment.

Hard coal such as anthracite yields a large quantity of coke and a limited amount of gas; soft bituminous coal does the reverse and Melton was supplied with a fairly soft Derbyshire 'gas' coal. Coal gas produced in retorts contains about 45% hydrogen and 35% methane or marsh gas, the latter having about three times the heating value of hydrogen; the rest is carbon dioxide, nitrogen and traces of other gases. Gas made by my plant's two tiny retorts was pumped first through a tar extractor, then a 'purifier' containing slaked lime, and thence into a small gas holder. Midlands coal contains about 14 lb of sulphur per ton and one of the purifier's functions was to remove

72

it but the equipment, apparently made by handymen in Melton works, tended to operate feebly and complaints from the householders that my gas begrimed their utensils with soot and clogged their lamps with stinking sulphurous crusts were frequent. I believe there is legislation prescribing the maximum amount of sulphur permitted in manufactured gas but I was never told about it. The carriage lighting gas was made from 'gas oil' delivered in tank wagons. The entire plant was run by one man who as far as I know was completely untrained and had learned gas manufacture from the previous holder of his office; I lived hoping that the gas put into the carriage tanks was pure and without air that would have rendered it highly explosive.

Because of the gradients, curves and mediocre permanent way, there was never any hope of a fast M&GN service. The lines west of South Lynn were virtually level across the Fens but Norfolk was different; Melton was almost on a summit approached from east and west by a four mile climb of 1 in 100, and from Cromer by a three mile ascent of 1 in 80. The last three miles from Norwich to Melton were almost as steeply uphill; in fact there were hardly any level stretches at all in Norfolk except for a couple of miles at the end of the Norwich branch. The poor state of the permanent way was the main reason for an accident on 20 August 1937 near Hindolveston when, at 12.7pm, a three coach passenger train hauled by D9 engine No 6013 became derailed on a 60 chain curve. There were no transitions at the ends of the curve, and the cant (the amount by which the outer rail of the curve was raised above the inner rail) which should have been 2in throughout was only $\frac{5}{8}$in in places; the pebble ballast was inadequately drained and the ground beneath soft and wet as a result.

The M&GN line having little in the way of earthworks, most of it following the contour of the land, there were not many overline bridges, which was probably why some Civil Engineer's men who raised and repacked a stretch of line between Melton and South Lynn forgot that they were reducing the clearance beneath a bridge when working under its arch. It was not long before the chimney of a D2 locomotive struck the arch a glancing blow and broke off; the appearance of this locomotive on entering Melton station must have been rather remindful of the spectral headless horse.

Coal deliveries to the shed had become very irregular and whenever possible coal had to be put into reserve by dumping it on spare ground in the disused works premises. Orders to dump came from the Doncaster Coal Office people and as they could usually foretell shortages they also notified us when we were to use our reserve stocks. It all involved considerable labour; the wagons had to be unloaded by hand and when word came to 'pick up', men had to shovel the dumped coal into empty trucks for shunting to the coal stage. I learned that the more coal we stored the better pleased the LRS in London would be, but a farce arose when, having dumped two or three hundred tons, orders came to 'pick up' and all the coal was shovelled back into the same wagons from which my men had thrown it the day before. After that it seemed rather pointless to unload the coal at all; I stored my spare loaded wagons in one of the disused works buildings and reported the contents, first as 'dumped' and in due course as 'picked up', and in the head offices happiness prevailed. Nobody seemed to worry as to the whereabouts of the wagons and that I was holding on to them.

Anything could happen on the M&GNR. Engine failures caused havoc to the service since a train that has stopped on a single line obstructs all the traffic in both directions. By 1945 the D1 and D2 engines, despised and disintegrating, and which set out with trains for Melton every day, were on their last legs, reeling and lurching as they rattled along and breaking down with depressing frequency; the driving wheels scraped across the bridle rods and sheared them apart, steam pipes broke in the smokeboxes, great splits occurred in the tender tanks that emptied all the water onto the track before the trains could reach the next station, and axlebox springs broke on almost every trip. As a Norwich inspector said, there was no time at Melton to plan improvements or to reorganise; it took every moment one had even to keep the trains running at all!

Station shunters marshalled the coal wagons in and out of the gas plant which was, however, some 15 to 20ft below main line level; the track leading to its coal siding was on a short and steep descent. I was not at all surprised when before long a drawbar broke and a 16 ton wagon of coal ran away from the locomotive that was lowering it, attained a frightening speed and smashed the buffer stop to pieces before its wheels sank into soft wet ground beyond. To lighten the vehicle sufficiently for the breakdown men to raise it with jacks the coal had to be unloaded into wheelbarrows and rerailing took two days.

Immediately after Christmas 1945 London became crowded with empty coal wagons that the collieries could not accept until mining was restarted after a fairly long miners' holiday. It was decided to store them for a week or so on a couple of miles of almost level double line between Melton and South Lynn, and one afternoon some 300 wagons were stabled on the down track, single line operation by pilotman being applied to the other. The traffic staff forgot, however, to leave gaps at the accommodation crossings where farmers needed to cross the railway and at dusk there were frantic telephone reports of cattle and farm machines stranded in the fields. No locomotive is capable of moving 300 wagons so spaces had to be made by taking an engine and tow rope onto the other line and shifting the trucks a few at a time; the operation, carried out in the dark, took several hours, with gruesome effects on the passenger service.

I left Melton in 1946, doing so, I rejoice to say, before the entire roof of the shed fell in early one morning, bringing down the walls as well and immobilising all the engines within the building. It was also before a goods train at Norwich City, the M&GN station, set off along a siding which the driver believed to be the main line, the engine breaking down the buffer stop and plunging into the River Wensum where it came to rest half engulfed in mud. Fortunately, neither caused any casualties.

The M&GNR no longer exists, except for a few fragments. Doubtless in its earlier days it played a part in getting Norfolk

and Lincolnshire farm produce to market, which was probably
its most important function, but every town it served, apart from
Holt and Holbeach, also had an LNER station, and many of its
rural stations lay long distances from the nearest villages; it
became a heavy liability to British Railways and on 28 February
1959 most of the wretched little line was closed and dismantled,
much of its formation having since merged into fields through
which it lay, to become farmland.

At Sutton Bridge two interesting relics remain. One is the
great swing bridge over the River Nene, named Cross Keys after
a hamlet two miles away; the station immediately to its west took
the name Sutton Bridge from the village that arose on the bank
after the river had first been spanned in the 19th Century. The
swinging section had three main lattice girders supporting two
decks, the upstream deck carrying the M&GN line in single track
form and the other a roadway. Brought into use in July 1897, the
bridge was paid for mostly or entirely by the Midland Railway;
the roadway, which is the A17, now occupies both decks.

The other leftover is the large abandoned dock which,
constructed with considerable assistance from the GNR, lies half
a mile downstream from the bridge. Almost 500 yards in length
and 200 across, it cost nearly £250,000; the GNR directors had
great hopes that it would take shipping from Wisbech and that
traders, instead of using the GER, would consign goods from
Sutton Bridge to the GNR at Peterborough, the line between the
two already being available. The dock was opened in the summer
of 1881 and one ship sailed in with a cargo of timber from
Norway but the very next day part of the dock wall gave way and
then most of the water leaked out every time the tide fell in the
river. Repairs were attempted but the defects were so serious that
it became clearly uneconomic to rectify them and the dock was
left to moulder away; it is now a golf course. The GNR lost
£55,000 in the venture, a sum equivalent to half a million
pounds today. Local people claim that a site near Cross Keys, on
the Lincolnshire – Norfolk border, is the place where, in 1216,
King John lost his valuables when journeying over the Wash.

5 Head Office

Melton was my last shed; I next became a head office technical assistant in the Locomotive Running Superintendent's headquarters at Hamilton House, adjoining Liverpool Street station. The LRS's personnel amounted to his Assistant, two technical assistants, and a small supporting secretarial and clerical staff; the more senior technical assistant dealt with locomotive affairs, and my duty as the second assistant was to handle all other engineering matters.

The papers that came to me mostly contained schemes submitted by the DLSs for structural improvements or alterations at running sheds, for which the General Manager's approval was necessary; the Civil and Electrical Engineers did normal maintenance work but required the GM's sanction for new construction. The schemes were generally very small; the War was only just over and money and materials were too scarce in 1946 for works of any magnitude. A scheme might, for example, propose the enlargement of an engine shed's tool store, involving the demolition of some brickwork, building a new wall, altering door and window positions, and moving a few water pipes. I would usually inspect the site, prepare drawings and get estimates from the Engineers. Then came the hardest part of all, which was the production of proof that the scheme would result in a saving; without it no scheme had any hope of getting the stamp of approval and the District Officer concerned would have to carry on as before, for he would not get any proposals sanctioned merely to make things easier or more comfortable for

77

the work force. A ready and unanswerable challenge was always at the GM's finger tips; 'how is it that you have been able to conduct your affairs without difficulty in the past?'

So we had to establish a saving in order to get anything improved at all. We had to 'show a saving' to provide an electric drill that would replace a manual appliance that toiling men had cranked the last hundred years. We had to 'show a saving' if some shed master wanted a telephone extension to avoid walking 200 yards to an instrument in a dingy storeroom every time a call came in. A saving had to be shown if a dungeon beneath a grimy coal stage or chilly water tank, and called an office, was to receive another window so that the clerk who spent his days there might see his papers properly. The ruses that I invented, often prompted by my chief, to create evidence of reduced expenditure that would convince the GM, or at least to fabricate an image of it, were ingenious, cunning and usually false; once the accountants had worked out the savings, however, based on what I told them, the GM generally asked a few questions and then gave the schemes his blessing.

Whereas a general lack of facilities prevailed at most ex GER sheds, anyone who up to 1953 paid a first visit to Ipswich depot came away appalled. The equipment for maintaining its 50 or 60 engines amounted to a shed providing cover for *two* locomotives, a few hovels that served as workshops, staff rooms and offices, and a large water tank beneath which a couple of dark and very damp chambers acted as store places for locomotive spares. There had never been a coaling plant and every bit of the 150 or so tons of coal that the engines consumed daily had to be shovelled direct from the wagons onto the tenders. Almost all fitting work had to be done out of doors. The depot had apparently been built by the Eastern Union Railway when the line was opened in 1846 and it lasted 107 years, along with its EUR methods of operation, until the entire premises were reconstructed in 1953 or thereabouts.

Not that such depressing conditions had gone unnoticed. Almost as soon as the GER had become a part of the LNER,

Gresley, the new CME, visited most of the principal locomotive depots, declared affairs at Ipswich to be a disgrace and announced the immediate preparation of a modernisation scheme. Other plans for Ipswich followed but unfortunately the schemes only developed on paper. There was never any real action and Gresley's interest soon waned; he hated the GE and wanted nothing to do with it, knowing that the railway had very good engines that probably surpassed anything ever produced at Doncaster, and despising it because it employed the Westinghouse brake and operated the biggest steam suburban service in the world, he having had little experience of intensive suburban traffic.

Shortly after World War II the great national master policy called Post War Planning was released, under which Ipswich depot could at last be rebuilt. One day I was told to find out what was needed to meet the requirements of the present and the future there; I was then to prepare sketches of a new layout and new buildings in sufficient detail to enable the Civil Engineer to produce working plans and estimates. I spent two or three days at Ipswich and then designed a really splendid new locomotive depot containing almost everything for the staff except sauna baths, but as far as I remember my plans were put and remained on top of a gigantic pile of earlier documents, all contained in a folder that bore the somewhat cheerless title 'Conditions at Ipswich Loco Shed'. It was only after nationalisation that reconstruction was taken in hand.

Most of the engine sheds throughout Britain were in a sadly run down state by the end of the War; even essential maintenance was very much overdue and staff who had to perform their work in flooded engine pits, in draughty sheds with leaking roofs and, in places, with no roof at all, were getting restless. New factories were opening with facilities so attractive that men became less and less inclined to take engine shed employment and to perform such filthy work as shovelling coal and ashes, cleaning engine flue tubes, or boiler washing with cold water. Fitters and mates became disheartened when they compared their duties on engines dripping with grease and grime with those of well-paid assembly plant operators. Moreover, the railways, becoming a butt for politics, were being deliberately starved of materials in order to ruin them and so strengthen the case for their nationalisation. The outcome was that the railway service as a whole deteriorated, all the more so because of the quality of the coal; whereas up to 1939 the railways bought high grade coal for passenger and express goods locomotives, during and after the War they had to take what was sent to them.

Liverpool Street's huge steam worked suburban service was run almost entirely by locomotives allocated to Stratford depot which, with about 400 engines, was the largest steam engine base in the world. Towards the end of 1946 this service, which I had to use daily, was breaking down into a fearsome state; train cancellations, engine failures and staff shortages were resulting in shocking unpunctuality and disgraceful overcrowding. The carriages, built for suburban traffic, had exceptionally narrow 12 seat compartments into each of which *23* people squeezed themselves in the peak periods, seven sitting along each side and nine standing, and sometimes even more. Drivers were having to stop their trains between stations to regain steam pressure and occasionally when trains were unusually delayed their engines ran short of water. Then the fitting staff at Stratford shed, impatient now that the War was over with an employer who left them to work in the drizzle or beneath cascades of rainwater that poured through holes in the roofs, to stand in wet, oily pools, and stumble over great heaps of ashes, discarded firebars and other oddments that perpetually littered the premises, announced that they would limit their output until their buildings were repaired and their conditions improved. The result was that the suburban service nearly collapsed altogether. Travelling became a ghastly nightmare and evening newspapers devoted columns to the misery of the office workers' daily journeys; one writer said that Goering and Himmler ought to be punished for their war crimes by being made to travel up and down between Liverpool Street and Romford in LNER third class carriages all day long for the rest of their lives, and *Punch* said 'the retreat from Moscow must have been quite a lark, compared with the advance to Gidea Park!' Eventually several MPs received so many angry letters from daily travellers that they had to act and the train running became the subject of a Parliamentary debate.

The debate took place in the House of Commons on 22 January 1947, being opened at 7.54pm by the MP for Hertford who called the Minister of Transport's attention to the persistent unpunctuality of the evening trains from Liverpool Street to Bishop's Stortford, only 30 miles away. He quoted the 6.30pm train that had arrived at Bishop's Stortford an *hour late* day after day, except those days when it was cancelled and didn't run at all; then he described the running of the 6.0pm train to Broxbourne, 17 miles from Liverpool Street, saying that it was 85 minutes late one day and cancelled the day after. The 5.42pm was 116 minutes late at Bishop's Stortford on 6 January and the 10.0pm train on the 12th did not get there until 6.0am next morning.

The MP for South East Essex then took up the attack and said that 'while the railway companies have, happily, regulations for safeguarding the humane loading of cattle, the passengers who are compelled to travel from Liverpool Street have certainly not been safeguarded by any such conditions'. 'If any military officers had been responsible during the War for loading troops in the manner in which civilians are now loaded at Liverpool Street every night, bowler hats would have been handed out'. At Liverpool Street, he said, there had been no real effort to advise the poor shambling passengers, trains had been cancelled without prior notification and passengers had been assembled in one train and then told to get out and take another.

The MP for Denbigh said he had visited Liverpool Street and had been appalled by what he saw; hundreds of people were attempting to get into trains that were already full with people standing in every compartment, and were still trying to get in when the train was beginning to move, and he believed that the lives of many people had been considerably shortened by the last few years' efforts of travelling. The MP for Hitchin said that no one in Hertfordshire who relied on the LNER could possibly make an appointment and be sure of keeping it. The MP for Southend-on-Sea asked the Minister to pay some attention to the appalling service between London and his town; one of his constituents, he said, had travelled home with 25 people in a compartment besides himself. The Belfast MP said that the passenger vehicles on the Liverpool Street line, known by the courtesy title of 'coaches' and so called by the railway, were dirty, uncomfortable and, he supposed, manufactured when railways first started to run; they were normally unheated and in cold weather never heated.

After many more MPs had spoken the Parliamentary Secretary to the Minister of Transport replied, first expressing unbounded admiration for the patience of the travellers at Liverpool Street where he had seen conditions for himself; then he praised the railway staff who operated the lines in the difficult prevailing conditions. He had to tell the House, however, that the prospects of any immediate substantial improvements were not very good. Several thousand more people were using Liverpool Street in 1947 than in 1938, the electrification work that had been started in or before 1938, and which should have been completed in 1940, had been postponed by the War, forcing the LNER to carry on with old rolling stock that new electric trains would have replaced. The disputes at Stratford had resulted in a third of the trains being cancelled and no engines could be spared to shunt carriages into sidings where cleaners could attend to them. 'We are fully aware', he said, 'that this is probably the worst passenger service in any part of the country and anything that can be done will be done to relieve the situation'. With that, the Debate ended, at 9.59pm.

Gradually the Liverpool Street services began to get better, improvements at Stratford, promised to the staff so often in the past but not commenced, at last being put in hand. The electrification was restarted but it took several more years to provide a punctual, frequent and fast service; even today in peak periods Liverpool Street station is worked to utter capacity, a difficulty being that whenever one of the lines into the country is given a better service builders at once respond by putting up more houses along the route until very soon the trains are as overfilled as they were before the improvements were made. More people travel on the line between Liverpool Street and Shenfield each working day than on any other line in Britain.

A betterment launched at the time of the debate had immediate effects, however. For a whole week inspectors rode on the engines of every suburban train in and out of Liverpool Street; they showed the enginemen how to get a little more out of their locomotives by expedient use of the valve gear and by improving their control of the fire, and timekeeping began to improve. Then the inspectors noticed that up morning trains often lost up to a minute at each station because the guards were not getting prompt 'all right' signals from the platform staff; trains were allowed to linger while last minute passengers ran through the booking halls and scrambled into compartments. It was arranged to close the gates as soon as the trains entered the stations and on the first morning when this was done scores of tardy passengers were shut out; next day all the tardy passengers reorganised their affairs and were already lined up along the platform when their trains drew in, and the small but cumulative station delays were eliminated.

The route from Liverpool Street to Colchester is the Eastern Counties Railway's earliest line and my spell at Head Office gave me ample opportunities to explore it. The Mile End to Romford section was opened in June 1839, and the rest was brought into use in stages until Colchester was reached in 1843, by which time the London terminus was at Shoreditch. The company's first main works buildings, where all locomotive and carriage repairs were carried out until the works at Stratford was opened in 1848, still stand on the up side of the main line about half a mile to the east of Gidea Park station.

The ECR adopted a 5ft gauge for the Colchester route but it is not certain why. Many early railway engineers spent much time deciding on the best gauge for their lines but their ponderings were needless as experience has shown that within reason any gauge is suitable for a train. What *was* important, as George Stephenson insisted at the very beginning, was that they should all be the same, sound and obvious advice that some engineers failed to heed. In 1844 the ECR converted its gauge to 4ft 8½in, the directors following advice by Robert Stephenson on the best method of doing it. On 2 November 1844 Capt J. Coddington reported to the Board of Trade that the conversion had been done in six weeks without stopping the traffic; one track was dealt with at a time, the trains using the other track which was provided with temporary sidings at intervals to serve as passing places. Workmen shifted the outer rail 3½ inches, so, it was claimed, 'adding stability to the embankments', and the turntables were fitted with special rails 1¾ inches wider than those laid originally. The rolling stock was altered similarly, half being dealt with at a time. A passenger who travels in the front of a train today between Shenfield and Colchester can readily see that the embankments are slightly wider than is usual and so are the original overline bridges.

The very first operations ever carried out in Great Britain by a mechanical excavator were on the ECR. In 1834 a young American engineer named William Otis invented the world's first steam excavating machine; it proved successful and in or about 1836 four more were built, one being brought to Great Britain and put to work in the cutting between Brentwood and Shenfield. It was somewhat primitive, with a frame and jib of timber, and lacking shelter for the engineman or his assistant who fired the vertical boiler, but its basic features, including the 'dipper handle' and bucket, have been followed ever since in excavator design. Major General Pasley inspected the line between Chelmsford and Colchester in July 1843 and said in his Report to the Board of Trade that the engineer:

> showed me an American machine for excavating earth, by the action of a steam engine, which forms part of it, and which he was using for the sake of experiment, in widening the deep cutting near

Brentwood. It forces a scoop into the earth, which acts upwards, filling itself, and when full, is turned round by a crane, and its contents, about 1¼ cubic yard of earth, are then discharged into a wagon of the usual form. This machine, invented by Mr Otis of New York, appears to me not only very ingenious, but efficient, for I think that it would remove with ease almost any sort of so⸱ that I have seen in railway cuttings, excepting rock or chalk.

The ECR was the first railway in the world to i in rails by means of fishplates. On all the early railways the rails were held by 'joint chairs' where they butted end to end, both ends being supported by the chair and the sleeper beneath. The rails being of iron, their ends were inclined to bend somewhat readily, not downwards but sideways, and so the rails, or their ends if they were fish bellied, were accordingly made with as little depth as the axleloads permitted; it might have been thought that the idea of bolting the rail ends together with fishplates was an obvious one but any drilling through shallow rail ends would have weakened them to excess. However, in 1847 an inventor, William B. Adams, patented the 'fish joint' and in 1849 James Samuel, the ECR's resident engineer from 1846 to 1850, fitted fishplates of his own design to a stretch of track between Shoreditch and Stratford. The rails were of iron and of 'double T' section, 5in deep and weighing 92 lb/yd. To prevent the ends from bending which, with a 5in depth, they were very liable to do, each outer fishplate had a foot that rested on a sleeper beneath the joint. The whole story of how the railway fishplate was developed is recorded in a paper read by Adams at the Institution of Civil Engineers; it can be found in Volume 11 of the Proceedings, and Volume 16 contains another paper on the same subject. It was many years, however, before all the railways adopted the 'fished joint'; the companies could not relay every track overnight. For a long time the BOT's Inspectors recommended rail joints secured by fishplates and in a Report by Capt G. Wynne on an accident that had occurred near Mossley, LNWR, on 10 April 1854, when a train ran off the track because a key had fallen out of a joint chair holding two adjacent rail ends, he said:

Would the accident have occurred had the rails been fished as is very generally the case throughout the LNWR lines? Certainly not. There can be no doubt that the practice of fishing the rails is a great element of safety and the principle cannot be too much encouraged.

Incidentally, both Adams and Samuel claimed to have invented the railway fishplate.

James Samuel was a pioneer in another field, namely locomotive compounding. In 1852, according to the Proceedings of the ICE, he converted a goods engine to work on the compound principle but how successful it was remains unknown. However, the Eastern Counties Railway takes the credit for the introduction of the first compound locomotive, a venture not repeated until 1866, in France.

Many of the older station buildings along the Colchester line almost certainly date from 1843, with various later modifications, but the finest ECR station in Essex is undoubtedly that at Maldon. The two branches from Witham to Maldon and Braintree respectively, and amounting to 12 miles of single line in all, were begun as one system by the Maldon, Witham and Braintree Railway which, however, was bought by the ECR almost as soon as construction began; it was opened in October 1848. MWB-ECR can still be read on the station's rainwater fall pipe heads and the building is being preserved; the original MWB terminus station at Braintree has long since been demolished.

Shortly after, I changed jobs again but this time I became a head office inspector at Liverpool Street, with decidedly unusual work; I was to accompany a two-coach Instruction Train to every running shed in the Southern and North Eastern Areas, giving technical lectures to the staff. The train was not new. One of the coaches, a 12 wheeled GER bogie saloon, carried an operational set of Westinghouse brake equipment and also two or three working vacuum cylinders; it had been the first instruction vehicle on any British railway. The other coach was a GCR luggage van converted into a lecture theatre with blackboard and seats, and containing specimens of locomotive

Above: Another type based at Lowestoft while the author was in charge there were Class E4 2–4–0s, similar to this example. (*L&GRP 13825*).
Below: For many years trains were hauled up Cowlairs incline out of Glasgow Queen Street by cable attached to the front of locomotives. At the summit it was self-releasing but there were occasional accidents as described on page 48. (*L&GRP 5557*).

Above: The LNER took over operation of the Midland & Great Northern line in 1936 and eventually sent some former GE 4–4–0s of LNER Class D16 of one or other variations of the type illustrated here to replace the ageing fleet of M&GN 4–4–0s. The D16s were mainly used on the heavier passenger trains while the author was in charge at Melton Constable in 1945 *(L&GRP 3451). Below:* The 13 acre dock at Sutton Bridge, Lincolnshire, constructed in 1881, never used and abandoned.

lubricators, injectors and many other fittings, most of which were full sized and sectioned or cut away to reveal their inner working parts. There were also four excellent sectioned scale model valve gears, two Stephenson's and two Walschaerts. On passing into LNER ownership the two vehicles were connected, with gangways, to form a train which was then sent on tours of the Southern Area, enginemen who visited it being more or less left to find things out for themselves; I was the first full time instructor.

And so began my first tour which, with some 90 sheds to visit, took about 18 months, spending perhaps ten days at each big shed and two or three at the smaller places. As far as possible the train spent a weekend at each depot so that I could instruct the local Mutual Improvement Classes, the voluntary organisations established by keen drivers; Sunday was the only day when most of the men could get together.

My daily routine was to open the train at about 10.0am; enginemen and shed staff visited it both in working hours and when off duty, examining the exhibits for themselves or letting me explain them. During the week I gave evening lectures to the MICs; on Sundays lectures often went on all day, the same lecture sometimes being given more than once. My discourses were on the working of boilers, valve gears, lubrication, train heating, and on Westinghouse and vacuum equipment; I also talked on Rules and Regulations, and on the working of single line railways, not realising at the time that in teaching the same Rules over and over again at shed after shed I was preparing myself in the best possible manner for another post that was soon to come my way.

Despite all the fancy teaching aids to be had, the old fashioned blackboard and chalk is still, I am convinced, the best medium for conveying subject matter to an audience, provided that the instructor writes plainly, has some ability to draw and uses yellow chalk which shows better on a blackboard than white. I had to keep in mind, however, that few of my class members had had opportunities of learning very much in the way of physics or science; whereas the Westinghouse brake was not hard to describe, before I could teach the working of vacuum brake equipment I had first to clarify the meaning of vacuum and to show why it is that the atmosphere presses at about 15 pounds per square inch on the earth's surface. To present a concise and accurate explanation of how a feed water injector, worked by steam, manages to put water into a boiler against steam pressure is most difficult; it is unrealistic to talk about kinetic energy and to display mathematics on the blackboard to men who want a simple description that they can remember readily.

To meet my students' needs I set about enlarging the collection of exhibits by having models for instruction purposes made from scrap equipment; they served well so long as they *looked* all right, whatever their condition, and I obtained fittings as I went from depot to depot, doing a good deal of the cutting, sectioning and painting myself. I also produced brief and sometimes illustrated descriptions of each model and put them into little glazed frames alongside the specimens. To improve my vacuum brake lectures I made a barometer and put it near my blackboard so that I could describe how the atmosphere's weight balanced and held up the 30in mercury column.

The work proved popular with the footplate staff, and within a year the General Manager authorised the addition of a third coach to the train, to accommodate a generator so that I could have ample lighting and could supplement the blackboard with a diascope by showing slides copied from text book drawings or which I could make myself. I even fitted a tiny workshop into the new coach where I could prepare new exhibits. The enthusiasm shown by locomotive men for the train after the enlargement was most gratifying and so was the respect for it that everyone displayed. I would leave it open and unattended for odd hours and never once in the $4\frac{1}{2}$ years that I supervised it was there any disturbance of its contents. I had a fairly large glass case taken from a store and turned it into a miniature museum displaying early Rule Books, timetables, circulars, and tools bearing names of pioneer railways. It attracted considerable attention.

At one depot a serious accident was avoided only by luck when an apprentice made a most foolish attempt to look inside a detonator; it exploded when he put it in a vice but he escaped with a few cuts although he might well have lost his eyesight. Hoping to satisfy people's curiosity I at once obtained the parts that go to make a detonator, except the gunpowder, and mounted them in a little case which, with a description to explain how detonators work, was put up in one of the coaches.

Papers dated 1844 preserved by the Department of Transport record how detonators came into being. They were introduced on the London & Birmingham Railway when trains were being worked entirely by the time interval system; a train that became delayed or broke down had a good chance of being run into by the following train, although the rules required a man to be sent back with a 'red lantern' to meet and stop any approaching train by showing his danger signal and 'by calling out to the driver'. A memorandum from the Inspector General of Railways said:

I ... beg leave to bring under your ... notice a very ingenious arrangement adopted on the London & Birmingham Railway, as a fog or danger signal, at the suggestion of Mr Cowper, son of the King's College professor of that name. This consists in sending a man back to place a small flat circular tin box containing a charge of gunpowder, mixed with a little fulminating powder, on the line of rails by which the next train is advancing; which box has two leaden fangs attached to it for clasping the rail, which at other times are doubled flat down upon the box to save room. As soon as the wheel of the locomotive engine of the approaching train passes over this box, it fires the charge, with an explosion sufficiently loud to be heard in the most stormy night, or in going through a tunnel; but not powerful enough to injure the rails or the wheels of the engine. Under the circumstances supposed, this arrangement as a signal of danger or caution, is preferable to a red light by night, or in a tunnel, because no neglect or inattention on the part of the engineman or fireman of the coming train can render it possible for them to pass without being aware of the explosion, which cannot fail to take place, and on hearing which it would be their duty to stop.

The memorandum recommended every railway to adopt 'the

new danger signal by means of gunpowder', which very soon they all did.

One day the Railway Executive's training and education officer arrived and with great self importance inspected my train, summarily declaring that it contained far too many exhibits. I was not surprised; he had designed two more recent trains and I was satisfied that mine was the best of the three. Then he turned to me; how came I to be on instruction duties when I had not been properly trained? A great oversight on someone's part, it seemed! Before long I was directed to attend a three months' course with 20 others at a BR college called Faverdale Hall, at Darlington, the building having originally, I was told, been the home of the NER's chief mechanical engineer. There we were required to learn a 'new' teaching method called 'Question and Answer'; instead of lecturing to his pupils the instructor had to make them participate by getting responses from them that were in fact the points that they were being taught. Perhaps it worked; I wasn't frightfully impressed. I don't think you can really *train* a teacher; the art of instruction is a *gift* possessed by some and not others, as I discovered both at school and at University all too readily.

Early in August 1948 I came to another turning point in my career; technical officers were required at the new Locomotive Testing Station at Rugby and I was recommended for one of the posts. A week or two later I was interviewed briefly by the Station's Superintending Engineer and selected.

6 Rugby Testing Station

The Testing Station was nearing completion when I reported to the Superintending Engineer in September 1948. It had been proposed many years earlier, Gresley being an initiator; he had observed the GWR's Swindon testing plant and the more modern French National Railways plant at Vitry, near Paris. Locomotives are tested to discover the causes of their shortcomings so that remedies and corrections can be applied. Steam engine tests were made as early as James Watt's days; he was a far more scientific man than most history books seem to appreciate and who realised that to improve engine design he needed to learn what went on in the cylinders. He invented the Indicator, the device that procures diagrams of the cylinder steam pressure variations throughout the piston strokes and which engineers have used ever since. Daniel Gooch, knowing that on a steam powered railway the coal bill is the second largest working expense, exceeded only by the wages account, made extensive trials with his early GWR engines to establish their performance in terms of fuel consumption.

The steam locomotive, regrettably, is very inefficient; only about 5% of the heat that the fuel releases is converted into useful work, the rest going up the chimney or radiating from the boiler. Even this poor result is obtainable only if the locomotive is designed correctly, and much design work of the past has been a matter of hit and miss. The grate must be of the right size although opinions have been divided on whether it should be long and narrow or short and wide. It must be able to get from beneath all the air needed to make the fuel burn thoroughly and the size and number of the boiler tubes must be sufficient for the fire's hot gases to give the water enough heat to make an adequate steam supply. Tubes that are too small cannot provide enough heating surface; too big, and the hot furnace gases will pass along them centrally without surrendering their heat.

George Stephenson produced the first locomotive boiler built on the principle of a firebox at the rear and flue tubes going through the water to a chimney at the front, a simple arrangement that has never been bettered. Locomotive design being based very much on maximum permissible axle loads, the boiler's size and weight must be kept within bounds. A Gresley A1 Pacific's boiler was about 6ft in diameter and $28\frac{1}{2}$ft in length but on all but the tiniest of locomotives the boilers are too small and must consequently be worked very hard; the fire of an express locomotive hauling a heavy train at speed needs to be white hot in order to keep the steam supply going.

Even a well designed boiler with adequate steam raising powers will not produce steam rapidly unless all its smokebox fittings are correctly fashioned. As the exhaust steam from the blast pipe escapes up the chimney it creates a vacuum in the smokebox that draws air through the grate into the firebox. But the blast pipe orifice must be in accurate alignment with the chimney and also of exactly the right size in order to obtain this vacuum, the dimension usually being determined by trial and error. Too large an orifice emits a sluggish blast that fails to produce vacuum but one that is too small throttles the exhaust and retards the engine. An excessive vacuum will draw unburnt fuel particles wastefully into the smokebox. On my Lowestoft F3 engines I found the ideal orifice to be $5\frac{5}{8}$in, provided by blast pipe liners, and no other size would do.

The ability of an engine adequately supplied with steam to generate hauling power depends largely on the layout and adjustment of the cylinder valve gear. The number of calculations, designs, lectures, papers and books that have been devoted to valve gears is beyond counting but in this field, too, trial and error have played a large part; a new valve arrangement may seem theoretically perfect but puts up a poor performance. Very often it has been possible to locate both boiler and engine faults only by analysing the results of tests, and it was largely for making such tests that the Rugby Testing Station was planned.

Many locomotives have been tested by working them on a train in the ordinary way with a dynamometer car containing equipment that gives a continuous indication of the locomotive's drawbar pull, the train speed, the distance travelled and, by connections to the locomotive, the boiler pressure, smokebox vacuum, and firebox temperatures. An observer riding with the driver records the cut-off positions and the handling of the engine in general. Unfortunately, such tests have to rely a good deal on information that may well be very inaccurate. The amounts of coal in the tender before and after the trial are usually determined somewhat crudely by weighing the fuel in bags on a portable scale, the amount used to get the engine to and from its train being guessed; dipstick readings of the tender tank levels are generally regarded as adequate for assessing the amount of water fed to the boiler, the amounts lost by injector overflow spillage remaining unknown. If a test involves several journeys, with the same engine or with two alternately for comparison, the train weights may not be consistent. And enginemen do not care for test work that involves the distracting presence on the footplate of a technical officer who is making notes or telephoning to the dynamometer car.

The weather may well affect running conditions during experiments carried out with trains and so may incidents on the line. One test on which I assisted when at Head Office and which involved, after much preparation, a run from Liverpool Street to Ely was completely spoiled because a cow was on the line and the train had to be stopped by a signalman and then taken through the section ahead at reduced speed. The results of such experiments have often been very questionable because the Officer detailed to carry them out has considered it advisable in the interests of his career to ensure that the Big Man by whom the trials were ordered received results that were expected; men who had trials to conduct thus became very discreet in this respect. Most tests that I saw on the LNER were almost absurdities on account of imprecision and prevailing influence.

A testing plant, however, enables an engine to be put through its paces under ideal conditions. The need to make complicated arrangements with the Traffic Department before any trials can be started does not arise, the speed at which the engine shall run and the load that it will work can be decided upon in advance, and throughout the test the engine speed and the load can be kept constant. Every measurement and assessment can be made accurately by suitably designed equipment and the absence of the wind resistance that affects a moving train is not so serious as to cause a testing station trial to fall short of reality. Finally, a team of technical officers at an establishment such as that at Rugby is not likely to be influenced into rendering untruthful reports.

The testing station scheme was hatched in 1936 by the LNER and LMS jointly; a site on the LMS at Rugby was chosen as it was readily accessible from all parts of the LMS system and from Peterborough on the LNER. Construction was started in 1938, suspended when war broke out, and resumed about 1947; by the time I had arrived at Rugby the Station had passed into the hands of British Railways. The main building, or test house, was of steel frame formation, 171ft long and $66\frac{1}{2}$ft wide; having some resemblance to a large cinema it was promptly named the Odeon by local people. Alongside it was a locomotive preparation shed with two tracks having inspection pits and water hydrants, as in a running shed, and with a 35 ton wheel drop to enable engine driving wheels to be taken out for examination or repair.

The principal feature of the plant within the test house was a pit containing seven pairs of rollers designed to support a locomotive without its tender; an 0–6–0 goods engine would require three of the pairs to carry it, a 4–6–2 Pacific would need six of which three would be revolved by the locomotive as soon as the driving wheels began to turn. Five of the roller sets were connected to hydraulic brakes that worked on the fluid flywheel principle and provided the loads for the locomotives under test; the remaining two were there to carry bogie or trailing wheels and did not normally revolve, five hydraulic brakes being sufficient as no engine having more than five coupled axles was ever likely to appear on British Railways. The plant was designed so that the drawbar of an engine on the rollers would be coupled to a fixed drawbar that was permanently attached to a very firmly anchored dynamometer; the drawbar kept the engine in position on the rollers and the dynamometer measured the drawbar pull exerted when the wheels were turning. The dynamometer was inside the lower chamber of a two-storey brick building within the test house, the upper storey containing a splendid soundproof control room having large windows that overlooked the test bed, and accommodating all the recording equipment.

In front of the control room and above the drawbar was the firing platform which carried a coal bunker and served as a tender when a locomotive was on the rollers; it rested on a weighing machine that enabled the weight of each load of coal carried by an overhead hoist to the bunker from a coal house to be recorded in the control room. Feed water for the locomotive injectors was supplied from calibrated tanks that were replenished from bigger tanks with 500 gallons of water at a time; there were other calibrated tanks for catching injector overflow water, so enabling the water put into the boilers to be measured accurately.

The control room's equipment was extensive. The main feature was the recording table, across which, during a test, a paper travelled slowly as it unwound from a roll driven through electric transmission by the locomotive wheels. A row of pens traced lines along the paper; one, operated by the dynamometer, recorded the drawbar pull in pounds and others alongside it automatically registered the power that was being developed, the work being done, and the locomotive's wheel rim speed, which was, of course, the equivalent of the locomotive's speed had it been travelling along a track. There were more pens which, operated by push buttons installed on the engine, could, by dabbing the paper, record such operations as spells of firing, injector operation or the adjustment of cut-off positions. The control room also had a series of instruments for connection to the locomotive under test, registering firebox, flue tube and smokebox gas temperatures, the steam pressures in the boiler, cylinders and exhaust passages, and the degrees of vacuum in the ashpan and the smokebox.

The hydraulic brakes which imposed a resistance representing that of a train enabled the load to be kept absolutely constant, if necessary for days or weeks on end. As the water circulating through the brakes was going to absorb all the work output of a locomotive on test, careful measurement of this water's increase in temperature would enable the hourly work output to be assessed; such a figure ought, of course, to be the same as the work output calculated from the drawbar pull and the distance that the locomotive was deemed to have travelled.

When a steam locomotive draws a train along a track it does not exert a steady pull on the coaches; it applies its hauling power in a series of jerks. Each movement of a piston under steam pressure causes a short sharp tug amounting to four pulls for every revolution of the driving wheels, or six if the engine has three cylinders. The action is like that of a boatman as he levers his craft along the water by successive oar strokes, or the repeated bouts of foot pressure exerted by a cyclist. When an engine is travelling at speed the impulses are rapid, perhaps as many as 20 to 30 a second, and the people in the train behind remain quite unaware of them; the tiny and momentary accelerations of the train caused by each piston stroke are rendered imperceptible by the vehicles' inertia, just as a heavy flywheel evens out the spasmodic piston thrusts and pulls of a stationary engine; for all practical purposes a train, because of its great mass, can be deemed to travel at an absolutely steady rate when hauled by a steam locomotive at a uniform speed.

But at a testing station a steam engine has neither a train to haul nor a flywheel to turn, the driving wheels of a powerful locomotive worked by high pressure steam being much too light to have any appreciable flywheel effect. The Rugby dynamometer was a cylinder containing a piston, the pressure of fluid within the cylinder indicating the engine's tractive effort. It was realised, of course, when designing the plant, that an engine's piston strokes would vibrate the dynamometer rather than exert a steady pull; to overcome this a special 'damping' appliance was provided in the form of an oil filled dashpot which was another cylinder containing a piston connected to the drawbar. The dashpot had a bypass passage through which the oil could be pushed from one end to the other should the piston vibrate as a result of rapid intermittent drawbar pulls by the engine; the intention was to restrict this passage, by valves operated electrically from the control room, until the engine's tractive effort became a steady draught. Unless all the shaking and vibration was effectively damped out the recording table pen that reproduced the drawbar pull would not trace a steady and even line.

Engines at work produce smoke and the test house required a chimney which projected through the fairly lofty roof but which would not, on account of its height, enhance the vacuum in the smokebox of the engine beneath it. The chimney that was installed was a steel tube four or five feet in diameter that could be moved longitudinally and thus positioned exactly above the chimney of a locomotive of any class or length; it worked very well and as far as I remember no traces of smoke or fumes were ever noticed within the building.

The Testing Station's authorised personnel amounted to the Superintending Engineer, his Assistant, about ten technical officers, of whom I and another were the two senior, a chemist, two clerical officers and two girl typists; then there were a couple of fitters, a chargeman fitter, two electricians, about three mates for these men, and two or three attendants who unloaded the coal wagons into the coal house, managed the Station's heating plant and generally kept the machinery and the premises clean and tidy.

It was intended that the Assistant would be in direct control of the tests. The senior technical officers were to manage the control desk, applying the load by operating the hydraulic brake equipment and manipulating the drawbar's steadying dashpot; their more junior colleagues would watch the recording table and note locomotive speeds, coal and water consumptions, temperatures taken at various points on the locomotive, feed water temperatures, the smokebox vacuum and so on. After a test it might be necessary to collect and measure the ash in the ashpan and smokebox of the engine concerned. The chemist's duties were to sample the coal and assess its calorific value, to analyse smokebox gases, examine smokebox ash for traces of unburned carbon and to study feed water qualities. If two engines were being tested for comparison the coal's calorific value might prove higher during one test than in the other and this would need to be allowed for, as would variations in feed water temperature.

Behind and alongside the control room were staff messrooms, a small fitters' workshop and another for the electricians. There was a laboratory for the chemist. The Station's main offices were contained in a small single storey building located about 100yd from the test house, which was reasonably distant from the noise of the plant; among the rooms was a large drawing office for the technical staff.

When I arrived at Rugby only a few of the staff had been appointed and I acted as the Assistant. As I appeared to be the only one there with running shed experience I was detailed to attend to practical matters and one of these was to choose applicants for the workshop vacancies; a number of men from other railway departments keen to obtain the chargeman's and fitters' positions came to me for interview and I found them all good and capable that it was far from easy to make selections. I also engaged two electricians. My next task was to equip the workshops and, acting a good deal on the chargeman's and electricians' advice, I ordered bench vices, tools and sufficient spare parts and stores to enable the Station's day to day duties to proceed without the need to beg and borrow from the nearby Rugby engine shed.

The fitters were required to do ordinary minor running repairs to the locomotives and to prepare them for tests by making temporary brackets and fixtures to carry wires and tubes that would lead from the boiler, smokebox or firebox to various meters and gauges. The electricians were to fit and connect such instruments as pyrometers and to maintain all the electrical equipment in the control room. It was found when testing began that our driver had very little to do except open the regulator when the signal to start was given and then to set the cut off to the position specified for the test, and, of course, be at the ready in case something arose that required the engine to be stopped immediately; firing, however, was particularly important and the value of the Station's results depended very much on the way in which the fires on the grates were controlled.

It was arranged that there would be a formal opening on 19 October 1948 by the Minister of Transport who would make a suitable inaugural speech and then by pulling a string cause an engine to be set in motion on the rollers for, officially, the first time. The Rugby Testing Station was the first new installation of any size on the railways since nationalisation in 1948 and the Railway Executive decided to introduce it to the world with much publicity. Hundreds of details still needed completion, however, and the preceding five or six weeks were devoted to a tremendous surge of work by the British Railways civil engineer appointed to supervise and guide the main contractor who had built the Station and his dozens of sub-contractors.

At last the time came, a week or two before opening day, when the roller test bed was ready to receive locomotives and we borrowed one from the engine shed and set about positioning it. To begin with we did not raise steam; the locomotive, without its tender, was pushed cold by another engine into the test house, in reverse. There was a special lifting table in the form of two beams that lay along the inner sides of the wheel rollers and placed so that the tyre flanges of an engine ran onto them. Before the engine actually moved onto the beams the rollers had to be positioned where they would be beneath the engine's wheels and we spaced them by measuring with a steel tape and clamped them down. As soon as the wheels were over the rollers the engine's drawbar had to be coupled to the dynamometer's permanent drawbar, which at first proved exceedingly difficult. The permanent drawbar could be raised or lowered to bring it level with any engine's dragbox; by dropping a 3in steel pin through both drawbars the attachment was complete. But the pin was a close fit and to shift the locomotive to and fro by fractions of an inch to make both holes align was almost impossible; however, I had a temporary tapered pin made at Derby which drew the holes together, and the working pin then went into place with ease.

Having anchored the engine, the next step was to set the wheels turning. Steam was raised in the preparation shed and a driver and fireman made the engine ready in the usual way, taking it out after the tender had been detached and then setting it back into the test house; we soon had it on the rollers, the moveable chimney properly positioned and the drawbars connected, when all was then ready for the very first run. The technicians went to their posts, a signal was given to the driver who then opened the regulator and the engine's driving wheels began to turn; we learned at once that some hydraulic braking was necessary at the outset to prevent the wheels from going round at speed but very shortly we had things nicely under control and the engine running slowly but steadily.

It was immediately apparent that there was something dreadfully wrong with the Testing Station's equipment. As the wheels continued to turn at a moderate rate the technician in charge of the dynamometer began to apply sufficient damping to eliminate the drawbar oscillation. But every time he increased the damping control the recording table pen displayed a rise in the drawbar pull although the pull was, in fact, remaining steady; as long as the dashpot held the oscillations in check the pen depicted a figure that was somewhat above the truth. This rather alarming feature remained a mystery until after I had left Rugby and as far as I know was never overcome; it did not, however, prevent useful work from being achieved as the error did not unduly affect comparative trials. The services of the Railway Technical Centre at Derby were called for; specialists who were sent made extensive experiments, setting up gauges, meters, balances, tubes of mercury and all the other paraphernalia of the scientist, and concluded that the trouble lay in the dashpot's bypass pipe. Turbulance in the oil as it was pushed from one end of the dashpot to the other interfered with the oil pressure induced in the dynamometer cylinder by the drawbar; a suggested remedy was a dashpot bypass so exquisitely streamlined that no turbulance would occur, a near impossibility in practice. The sad fact was that the drawbar equipment was not really capable of converting the intermittent impulses of a pair or trio of pistons into a steady and constant tensile force. As I have already said, a heavy train behind a moving locomotive's drawbar will do this, rendering all impulses virtually undetectable, and so will a big flywheel, but not a dashpot.

The Testing Station's precise purpose did not seem to be very clear at the time of opening. Originally the search for locomotive efficiency was the intention, efficiency meaning the amount of work done by an engine for every ton of coal consumed, but by 1948 it was already well known that there was little prospect of improving the 5% that was the efficiency of most locomotives. Then the Railway Executive said they would order wholesale testing of engines with a view of picking out any classes found to be unduly heavy on coal and scrapping them; most of the work that was ultimately done was the examination and elimination of defects in new engines designed and built by the Executive as standard types.

On the morning of 19 October I and my colleagues had to be on duty very early to get everything ready. In the office block the rooms were tidied; impressive drawings and sheets of calculations were laid out on the tables, together with mathematical books, instruments and slide rules, as if deep investigations were already in progress. The locomotive chosen for the ceremony, A4 Class No 60007, *Sir Nigel Gresley,* which had arrived from Peterborough the previous day, was steamed and carefully prepared by the King's Cross driver who had brought it over and who was well experienced in all kinds of testing and dynamometer car work. The test bed rollers were carefully set to receive it; in the control room the recording table with its pens and paper roll were thoroughly checked, and I visited the workshops and preparation shed to see that they were in order, with just sufficient tools laid out to give the impression that the establishment was really in business.

I doubt whether there has ever been such a gathering of principal railway officers before or since as the assemblage present at Rugby on the great day. All or at least most of the chief guests, including Mr Alfred Barnes, the Minister of Transport, and Sir Eustace Missenden, the Chairman of the Railway Executive, were to travel from London by a special train which I believe drew up on a line alongside the Testing Station, for I never saw it, being at my post within the building when it came. During the morning cinema newsreel teams arrived and set up their cameras and lighting equipment. A nurseryman's lorry appeared and within ten minutes strips of untidy soil outside the office block doorway had become gardens, displaying glorious arrangements of shrubs in buried pots and all to be taken up again the same evening after the last guests had gone. Every contractor hurriedly finished his last minute tasks, this scamper going on until just before the Great Train's arrival.

There very nearly wasn't any opening ceremony. When No 60007 steamed slowly out of the preparation shed on its way to the test house, about an hour before the Great Train was timed to appear, two sets of hand points had to be negotiated. Because of difficulties in getting supplies, however, these points had not been provided with levers and were being kept secured by wooden chocks. Permanent way men armed with hammers were

Above: The Edinburgh & Northern Railway's Burntisland terminus of 1847, as seen in 1978. The train that fell from the Tay Bridge in 1879 left here at 5.27 pm on that stormy December afternoon. *Below:* The Edinburgh & Glasgow Railway's Haymarket terminus, much the same today as when opened in 1842.

Above: The first locomotive works of the Eastern Counties Railway, opened in 1839; the building still stands, near Gidea Park station. *Below:* An early GNR 'joint' chair, designed to support a fishplate; observed at Boston in 1977.

responsible for setting the route correctly and placing the chocks but there must have been too many people giving orders to the driver and No 60007 ran through a set of trailing points when they were chocked the wrong way, each right hand wheel in the direction of travel bumping in turn over the closed switch blade. The Hand of Providence surely saved No 60007 from derailment that day and we all resumed our suspended breathing when it was safely inside the test house. It was promptly coupled to the drawbar and run for about ten minutes to enable the King's Cross driver to learn just how it behaved on the rollers, the technical boys satisfying themselves that the recording table worked properly. The driver was thoroughly briefed, the cord to be pulled from the balcony in front of the control room was tied to the engine whistle and every man then went to his appointed place to await the Minister and the guests.

The Train drew up and a few minutes later the test house was filled with three or four hundred people. Sir Eustace Missenden, who had until recently been the very successful General Manager of the Southern Railway, started the proceedings from the balcony by introducing the Minister, paying mighty tributes to the late Sir Nigel Gresley and to Sir William Stanier, reminding all who stood before him that Rugby's association with railways went back to the time of the Stephensons, and expressing his confidence that the Testing Station would prove invaluable in the furthering of locomotive designs and practices which had always led in Great Britain ever since the railway engine was first invented there. Then the Minister stepped forward amidst great applause and the two men on the footplate of No 60007 carefully adjusted their fire so that there would be just the right amount of steam to run the engine at a fair speed within ten minutes or so which was the anticipated length of the opening speech about to be given.

But the Minister did not confine his address to ten minutes but went on, and on, and on; he gave his listeners a full account of the nationalisation of the railways, why they had been nationalised, the great wisdom of the policy of nationalising and the huge interest that the public was taking in British Railways now that they had been nationalised. He then went through the whole history of the Testing Station, drew special attention to the fact that it was now being opened as one of the first major technical installations to be provided on the railways since nationalisation and that it displayed proof that the country was playing a leading part in industrial development. The speech was then extended to a dissertation on the great roads development scheme which was going to be put in hand by the Government which, along with the nationalised railways, would give the country the finest transport system in the world. And so on and so forth.

No 60007's driver, however, was not listening to the Minister at all, being much more concerned about his boiler pressure gauge, the needle of which was getting perilously near to blowing off point; traces of steam were, indeed, beginning to escape from the Ross pop safety valves which, had they opened, would have interrupted the Great Speech in a manner by no means common when Ministers are giving addresses. Fortunately the driver's very skilful and silent application of an injector kept the steam pressure steady but his watchful eye was also on the water gauges as any undue addition to the water level could well have resulted in the emission of quantities of dirty water from the chimney when the wheels began to turn, with effects on the hundreds of people standing around which would have been uncomfortable, to say the least.

At last the Minister finished what he had to say, declared the Station open and, grasping the cord, sounded a prolonged blast on the engine's triple chime whistle; the driver opened the regulator and the wheels of No 60007 began to move, the film cameras going into action as the great event unfolded. The number of prominent railway engineers present was almost endless; there was Sir Alan Mount, of the Ministry of Transport, most of the British Transport Commission members, almost all the officers of the Railway Executive, a big representation of Mechanical Engineers and Running Superintendents of all the

108

Regions, and many locomotive engineers from overseas. To sum up, the Opening Day was a great success.

The ceremonies over, we had to return to work, for there were proving tests to carry out before British Railways finally accepted the plant. We obtained a WD class 2–10–0 tender locomotive, this being the only type available to us that could work all five hydraulic brakes at once. The workmanship of the Station's equipment was of a very high standard but it was necessary to test officially every function for which the plant was designed to perform. Our 2–10–0 was worked on the rollers for several successive days at varying speeds and sometimes turning against a load well beyond the greatest train load that it would ever be likely to get on the railway, with two firemen taking turns to keep pace with its tremendous work output. I occasionally gazed into the dazzling white hot furnace feeling a little apprehensive about three longitudinal water tubes within the firebox, knowing as I did that they were carrying pressurised water at about 400°F amidst the terrific heat, and my trepidations were not groundless; a few years later I was to have dealings with an incident concerning such tubes on a similar engine, as will be told.

The 2–10–0's heavy working produced vast clouds of black smoke which drifted from the test house chimney, enveloping the southern half of Rugby, and not surprisingly brought representations from the town authorities. We managed to quieten the civic officials by telling them that the test in hand was exceptional and that normal work would result in nothing more than the discharge of a little steam; actually our main hope was that on most days the wind would be south westerly, its prevailing direction, and would blow our smoke away from the streets.

We could stand on the gangways alongside the rollers and watch the WD's wheels as they turned. Even under the heaviest loading there were never any signs of wheel slip on the rollers, the tyres gripping them as well as if they had been on ordinary dry rails; since there were no track undulations, the engine rode with perfect steadiness in the vertical plane but at certain speeds there would sometimes be a sideways swinging motion although not to any alarming degree. The brake hangers, their rods and brake beams, all of which swung loosely while the engine worked, swayed about considerably, however, and we realised that on any locomotive all the extensive wear that brake gear sustains is due almost entirely to the swinging and lurching of the parts; ordinary brake applications probably contribute very little to it. A more solemn feature was that the cylinder castings were loose on the engine frames, despite the 30 or 40 stout well fitted bolts by which each was secured; as the pistons worked to and fro the cylinders shifted about an eighth of an inch at each stroke and on any engine having such a weakness it would be quite pointless to set the valves to within degrees of accuracy of 1/64in which is the usual aim of most valve setters.

Apart from the difficulties with the dashpot, the trials confirmed that all the equipment was in order, a few trifling faults here and there soon being put right. The Testing Station was on the whole a splendid centre of research but it came, alas, too late to be of much avail; the first main line diesel locomotive had already been built and barely 20 years after the opening ceremony British Railways withdrew its last main line steam locomotive from service. My own view, based on my running shed experiences, is that although steam engine efficiency is most desirable, having regard to the cost of coal, and although engines must steam freely if they are to be functional, the CMEs of the Railway Executive and the Regions would have been doing far better had they concentrated more on producing locomotives that could be relied upon to work without falling to pieces on the line. What is the use of a grand engine capable of running at 120mph or more with a minimum of coal consumption if the driver cannot trust its connecting rods, valve gears or slide bars to hold together until he reaches his destination?

7 I Become a Civil Servant

Early in 1953 the Ministry of Transport (MOT) informed the Railway Executive that a candidate was required for a post in the Railway Inspectorate. I was advised to apply for it and did so as soon as a press advertisement appeared, the Executive gave me a good recommendation and I was called by the Civil Service Commission for interview. The audition was successful and I was selected as a Railway Employment Inspector; on Monday morning 9 November 1953, I commenced my 25 years as a civil servant by reporting to Lt-Col G.R.S. Wilson, the Chief Inspecting Officer of Railways, in Berkeley Square, London.

Young men seeking promotion are often put in a dilemma at interviews by being asked 'why did you apply for this post?' Their reply should never be that they seek higher salary but that the post offers *more important work;* this is what I told Lt-Col Wilson and maybe that is why I was chosen by the panel!

I had never seen the like of the MOT before, so different was it from the railway offices I had known. It had an imposing entrance hall, fast lifts, smartly uniformed messengers, a superb library with hundreds of railway books, an excellent dining room, and a first aid room with a nurse in attendance; I could almost hear the nightingale in the plane trees outside!

So many people have distorted notions about Ministries, gained from the Press, cartoonists and comic stage and radio performances. Dickens made inoffensive fun of government offices in *Little Dorrit,* and writers and comedians have been doing so ever since; from time to time, however, there are

111

particularly vitriolic attacks on civil servants that give the public bad and wrong impressions. Civil servants do occasionally make mistakes but are no different in this respect from the rest of mankind and in the main they do their work just as well as anyone else.

Civil servants, described by the Oxford Dictionary as 'members of the non-warlike branches of state administration', are appointed to assist Her Majesty's Ministers to carry out functions laid down for them by Parliament under various Acts. The Income Tax Inspector collects taxes, and the Customs Officer the duties that people owe on imported goods, because Acts of Parliament require this to be done and provide the necessary authority. A civil servant cannot, however, go beyond his powers; he is not a bureaucratic official holding authority to probe at large into people's affairs and business. The Civil Service today is large, employing some 750,000 men and women, but its growth during the last 100 years has been due to the increasing complications of life; electricity, radio, the motor car and the aeroplane are a few of the discoveries and inventions that have brought countless problems, making numerous Government controls absolutely essential in the interests of safe and peaceful living. The expansion of such social services as the administration of health facilities, pensions and education has also enlarged the Civil Service.

Each Department of the Civil Service is headed by a Secretary of State, a Minister, or by a Board, Commission or similar authority. There are also smaller parts called Offices, such as the Public Records Office or the Patent Office. Each Department or Ministry is usually organised in Directorates, Divisions, Branches and Sections; Departments and Ministries may be amalgamated or divided, and their Divisions may be transferred from one Department to another; such alterations become necessary now and then due to changes made in the country's legislation to meet new and altering situations. Thus, on 1 October 1953, five weeks before I entered the Civil Service, the MOT was united with the Ministry of Civil Aviation and I actually joined the MOT&CA; on 14 October 1959 they separated once more. *Whitaker's Almanack* gives details of all Government Departments.

The Railway Inspectorate (RI) is a Division and in 1953 its staff consisted of the Chief Inspecting Officer (CIO), three Inspecting Officers (IO), four Employment Inspectors (EI) and a small supporting staff of clerical officers and girl secretaries. The IOs were and still are officers drawn from the Royal Engineers, and if anyone imagines that these men are pensioned off military gentlemen of the 'club lounge' or 'Dad's Army' types often depicted on stage or screen, or favourites of some sort pushed into cushy posts by influential civil servants or members of the House of Lords, let me at once correct any such ideas. Every IO, past or present, has been or is an engineer highly knowledgeable in all the aspects of railway construction and operation, and this was something that I swiftly discovered for myself when Lt-Col Wilson, assisted by two staff officers whose identities I did not learn, interviewed me for the RI vacancy; never have I had such a stream of searching questions put to me at any interview as on that day. Influence and favouritism do not play any part in Civil Service appointments or advancements; everyone in the Service is free to apply for vacancies but choices are made by selection or promotion boards, consisting of three or four interviewers who for the most part are unacquainted with the candidate. The general system for promotion among already established staff is to select men by interview and then promote them when vacancies in the higher grades arise.

I soon learned how the MOT&CA was managed internally. The Establishment Division handled all personnel matters, to whom officers such as the CIO could make only recommendations; 'Establishment' gave all the decisions. The Accommodation Division allocated offices and provided furniture, and the Offices Services Division managed the heating and cleaning of the rooms. The Ministry of Works kept a small staff of joiners and electricians for general maintenance. Typing was done by 'pools'; a man had to be of pretty high status to be entitled to a personal secretary. A Press Office was responsible for the release of information to the newspapers and one of the press officers' tasks was to study the daily papers, cut out all items having a bearing on the Ministry or its work and to send them to the appropriate Divisions. Every newspaper feature on railways was sent to Lt-Col Wilson.

Weekend and after hours social activities among the staff are given considerable encouragement by the Civil Service, a feature that is all the more important in offices where much of the work is clerical, unavoidably repetitive and occasionally a little dull; I was amazed by the number of clubs and societies in the MOT. There were clubs for every kind of sport, there were chess clubs, stamp collectors' clubs, operatic societies and an art club that had an annual exhibition of really splendid pictures, to mention but a few.

How comes it that a Government Department has anything at all to do with the running of Britain's railways, when the railway Regions already have competent General Managers and engineers? The story goes back to the year 1839 and is related to the beginning of railways before that. The idea of laying a railway line was already old when George Stephenson was born; the need to find better ways of moving coal from a mine than in packhorse baskets led, in about the 17th century, to the laying of a rough track on the form of a plate way or rail way. The first tracks were of timber baulks which were later improved by iron plates laid along them (whence the name 'platelayer'); the next step was to put cast iron rails on stone block sleepers. The first motive power unit was, of course, the horse but in about 1800 crude steam locomotives began to appear. At first it was touch and go whether locomotives could do any better than horses but as coal mines close to canals or harbours became exhausted, new pits further away were opened up; they needed longer railways on which locomotives began to show their superiority. A shortage of horses which arose during the Napoleonic Wars when the Army took the best animals and all the fodder it could get helped the locomotive to establish itself; by 1820 several railways were operating in Britain's colliery and quarrying areas, using either horses or locomotives or both. In 1825 the 27 mile Stockton & Darlington Railway was opened, connecting Witton Park Colliery with a quay at Stockton from where coal could be shipped, mostly to London.

The Liverpool & Manchester Railway, opened on 15 September 1830, really started the railway age; it had a 31 mile double track main line and was the first inter-city railway system in the world. Soon other similar railways appeared; indeed, many were already being planned before the L&MR was finished. By the end of 1837 there were 540 miles of railway operating in Great Britain and many more lines were under construction; by the end of 1839 the operational mileage was 970 and only five years later it was over 2,200. Once the L&MR had proved itself railways spread very rapidly, a railway map of 1839 showing that Manchester, Liverpool, Preston and Nottingham were connected to a main line that led to Birmingham and London; a line from Carlisle to Newcastle joined several lines in Co Durham, London was almost linked with Southampton, and the Great Western Railway's first 31 miles were open.

In the earliest days of railways there probably was not much concern about safety. The first steam locomotives hauled their mineral trains at speeds of up to about four miles an hour which, to begin with, was considered satisfactory and as long as men kept out of their way they were not likely to come to harm. No doubt there were derailments and maybe engines occasionally overturned as a result but the age was one when it was accepted that industry claimed a number of lives every year; provided that things did not get unduly out of hand the hazards of railway work were probably borne without comment. But when the first main line railways came into operation it was quickly found that trains could reach speeds never before attained in the world. People soon adapted themselves to the 20, 30 and then 40mph journeys which within a few years the railways were providing; train travel became commonplace and to cope with increasing passenger traffic the companies ran more trains. Very soon it began to be realised that safety was something that needed serious attention.

The rapid development of railways was handicapped by grave shortages of men competent to run them. General managers who had hardly ever seen a train were appointed to superintend main lines, men whose previous work had been confined to the handling of horses were engaged as engine drivers, firemen and guards, and permanent way men were recruited from the farms. These men, unqualified through no fault of their own and supervised by staff equally inexperienced, operated railways that were virtually without signalling installations and worked trains that lacked brakes except for hand brakes in guards' vans and on locomotive tenders; locomotive design advanced far more rapidly than permanent way improvements and before long the tracks, of iron rails imperfectly secured at their ends by 'joint chairs', were having to stand up to ever increasing train weights and speeds for which they had not been fashioned. The operating instructions, if any, were contained in primitive rule books based on instructions carried by stage coach guards that dealt mostly with staff conduct. Regulations for running trains, hand signalling, station work and shunting were made by the men themselves as they gradually gained experience, and the outcome of such circumstances was inevitable; accidents in the form of collisions and derailments became alarmingly frequent.

Something else began to attract people's attention and, in turn, that of the Government; fears developed that the railway companies were building up transport monopolies as both passenger and goods traffic passed into their hands, ruining the canal owners, coach operators and innkeepers along roads parallel to railway routes. Furthermore, dangers were foreseen of huge financial losses as a result of lines being built at such expense that the owning companies could never pay a reasonable dividend, or worse still, of lines being started and then abandoned through lack of money to finish them. In the canal 'mania' of some 30 years earlier this had already happened; the Salisbury & Southampton, the Dorset & Somerset, the

Leominster and the Charnwood canals, to mention a few, had either been constructed only in part or else given up half excavated, leaving shareholders utterly ruined. Yet another anticipated possibility was that the directors of new railways, naturally anxious to obtain revenue, might open lines to traffic before they were properly finished, with assurances of completing the works as soon as finances permitted, a state of affairs that would not be at all conducive to safety.

Parliament, perplexed by these new problems, took a first step towards meeting them by appointing a Select Committee in 1839 'to enquire into the state of communication by railways', leaving it to the Committee to decide on the aspects to be examined; the Committee set to work, took a great deal of evidence from directors and principal railway officers and produced a report that dealt mostly with financial features but suggested the establishment of a board to deal with complaints and inter-company disputes, and recommended the inspection of new railways before opening. The Committee produced five more reports in 1840, of which the third recommended that Government control of railways should be kept to a minimum and that the working of the lines should be left to the companies owning them but suggested the creation of a Government Department to send inspectors to examine new railways. Parliament responded by passing the Regulation of Railways Act of 1840, authorising the appointment of inspectors with duties to inspect new railways, and laying down that railway companies were to send returns of all accidents involving personal injury.

This was the start of the Railway Inspectorate which, since its formation in 1840, has been responsible to Her Majesty's Government for safety on the railways down to the present day, including the Irish railways until the end of 1921; it is the second oldest technical Division in the Civil Service, being four years younger than the Factory Inspectorate which was the first. It has three principal duties, namely: 1) the inspection of new lines before they are opened, or of major alterations to existing lines, and of new signalling layouts; 2) the investigation of accidents by holding Inquiries; and 3) the provision of an advisory service for the benefit of the Minister or Secretary of State, which means giving technical guidance when new legislation is being drafted. The RI began as a Division of the Board of Trade and remained so until 1919 when it was transferred to the Ministry of Transport established that year.

The first inspection of a railway was in 1840 when an IO or Inspector General of Railways as he was then called examined a $6\frac{1}{2}$ mile stretch of the Birmingham & Gloucester Railway that was ready for opening; the line was found to be in good order, the company's directors were delighted and began to work trains along it a couple of days later. But when a further eight miles were inspected the works were found to be so unfinished that the BOT asked the directors to postpone the opening; the directors thereupon defied the BOT and declared the line to be available to the public. As a result the Government drafted another Regulation of Railways Act which became law in 1842, giving the BOT powers to defer the opening of a railway until the Inspector General was satisfied that it was safe for the working of trains.

Railway Acts are in two forms, the two Regulation of Railways Acts being General Acts, that is to say they applied to all railways. General Railway Acts may be said to have begun in 1830 with the Carriers Act which was drafted mainly for stage coach and carriers' cart transport but included railways; it is principally concerned with liability for lost goods and associated matters. Then came the Parliamentary Deposits Act of 1837, the Special Constables Act of 1838 and the Railways (Conveyance of Mails) Act of 1838 by which the Postmaster General was empowered to require the railway companies to convey mails and to provide separate carriages for letter sorting; this was followed by the Highway (Railway Crossings) Act of 1839 that laid down for the first time that a railway company was to maintain gates at places where its lines crossed roadways. No fewer than 121 General Acts on railway matters had been passed by Parliament by the end of 1909.

The Acts under which Railways have been constructed are Local Acts. The very earliest short coal-transporting plateways, often called tramroads, were as a rule laid either by the colliery proprietors or by arrangements of wayleaves drawn up with the landowners. But when longer routes were planned the promoters began to strike difficulties; some landowners were unco-operative and objections were raised and problems encountered when it was proposed to put lines across roads or rivers. The only way, then, to get a railway constructed was first to obtain Parliamentary sanction for the work; plans showing the route, its gradients and the manner in which roads and rivers were to be crossed had to be put up to Parliament, along with an appropriate Bill, so that as soon as the Royal Assent was obtained the construction of the line became legally approved and could go ahead.

Some of the Local Acts obtained for early canal construction included authority to lay short feeder railways or tramroads; for example there is an Act of 1790 'for making and maintaining a Navigable Communication between the Loughborough Canal and the Town of Leicester, and for making and maintaining a Communication by Railways, or Stone Roads, and Water levels from several places and mines to the said Loughborough Canal'. All such railways were, however, private lines for mine or canal proprietors' use but in 1801 an Act appeared authorising the Surrey Iron Railway Company to construct a $9\frac{1}{2}$ mile 4ft gauge line from the Thames at Wandsworth to Croydon which was to be a public railway, available by law to any user on payment of charges that the Act prescribed. The actual date of the SIR Act was 21 May 1801 and from that day onwards more Local Acts for public railways were obtained, a few annually at first, then dozens and a record 272 in 1846. I do not know whether anyone has ever counted all the Railway Local Acts but they include initial Acts to get railways started and further Acts authorising deviations even while construction was in hand, yet more Acts authorising companies to raise additional capital, to make branches, to abandon sections or branches already sanctioned and so on. All the Local Railway Acts are kept in the RI's strong room, the bound volumes occupying about 30ft of shelving.

Since 1842 the IOs have examined every new piece of railway but, to save the opening of new lines from being delayed should some deficiency be revealed by the inspection, the RI drew up a list of Requirements in 1858 so that railway builders might know in advance what the BOT Officers would be looking for on inspection day. There have been several editions of the Requirements since; the current edition can be bought by anyone from HM Stationery Office. The Requirements are not legal demands but the opening of a new railway for passenger traffic would not be allowed unless they have been met; among them is one to the effect that single line passenger railways must be worked by the token system or by the more modern tokenless block method.

Inquiries into railway accidents also began in 1840 and the very first of the thousands held since that date was into a passenger vehicle derailment about $\frac{3}{4}$ mile to the west of Howden station on the Hull & Selby Railway, on 7 August 1840 which was about five weeks after the line had been opened; it caused the death of four passengers. Lt-Col Sir Frederick Smith carried out the investigations, also dealing with another accident that occurred on the same railway at Hull on 7 September, fortunately without fatalities. The directive to Smith was that he should 'report his opinion on the precautions proper to be taken in order to guard against the recurrence of similar disasters in future'. The train that came to grief at Howden had eight carriages and a luggage van, almost certainly all four wheeled vehicles, but there was also a goods truck immediately behind the engine carrying a $2\frac{1}{2}$ ton casting; presumably the truck was a flat vehicle as, on approaching Howden, the casting fell off, derailing and severely damaging several of the carriages behind. Smith did not have far to look for the cause; the casting had not been lashed down or secured in any way, and no doubt the H&SR, comprehending for the first time that heavy pieces of equipment need to be fastened to wagons that are going to carry them, issued suitable instructions and provided ropes and chains.

The Hull accident reveals just to what extent the 'operating department' was learning as it went along; the running of trains being a new profession in 1840, neither staff nor supervisors had any sources from which to seek guidance. There were as yet no experienced inspectors to help the drivers, guards and station staff, no trained carriage and wagon men and no knowledgeable fitters and boilersmiths. What happened at Hull was that a mixed train – a train of both passenger and goods vehicles – was entering the terminus when, about 500yd from the end of the line, the driver detached his engine and ran it into a siding ahead, leaving the train to gravitate into the station on its own. None of the carriages had brakes and the guard was in a first class compartment so presumably there was not a brake van; the train collided with the station's end wall and broke it down, injuring a number of passengers. The records do not tell us how the driver unhooked the coupling or who reversed the points as the engineless train approached them; what they do say is that the engine driver had been driving passenger trains only two months and that his entire driving experience before that amounted to three weeks at the controls of a ballast train engine. Smith wrote in his Report 'that this is not a solitary instance of the employment of unskilful persons as enginemen and it is to be feared that the further the railway system is extended the greater will be the facility for inexperienced men getting employment in these highly important situations'. As for the lack of a brake he added that 'the proper place to use the brake is on the hinder passenger carriage – to run a train without a brake is very unsafe and the public should not be exposed to such risks'.

Only 12 days after the Howden accident the Eastern Counties Railway ran into trouble at Brentwood. On 19 August 1840 a train of five carriages and two trucks, with a stage coach on each, left Brentwood for London but had gone only a mile or so when it became derailed on a falling gradient that extended two miles in the London direction at 1 in 100, more or less the same as it is today. The four wheeled engine weighing 13 tons, its tender and three carriages went down the side of an embankment, both enginemen and two passengers being killed. Lt-Col Thomson who held an Inquiry into the accident concluded that the train was being worked at excessive speed and also commented on the light nature of the permanent way, laid with 15ft rails at 72 lb/yd in unduly small chairs. The company's directors admitted that the driver had obtained his experience by working ballast trains, as had the H&SR driver, but pleaded difficulties in getting competent enginemen due to the great demand for such men that was developing.

Thomson also inquired into a rear end collision that, on 13 September 1840, had added another blot to the ECR's record; the 2.0pm passenger train from the company's London terminus made a scheduled stop at Old Ford station about a mile along the line and while it was standing there an engine hauling a first class carriage approached along the same line and ran into it. It was unfortunate that the six persons who occupied the carriage included the company's chief engineer. Thomson's Report covered both accidents and concluded with a list of nine recommendations for the ECR's Board of Directors to consider:

1 A school should be formed for the education of enginemen where they may be instructed in the principles on which the steam engine acts and be made acquainted with its hand gear so that they may be enabled to start, back or stop the engine.

2 A maximum speed limit should be 'regulated from authority'.

3 That no railway should be opened for passenger traffic 'until both lines of rails shall have been laid'. (The Brentwood accident occurred on a stretch along which only one track had been completed, the other still being under construction).

4 That when notice is given by a railway company of their intention to open a new railway they should be requested to send a section of their rails and a sample of their chairs (presumably to the BOT).

Above: Brentwood station before the first world war. The original Eastern Counties Railway station buildings on the down (left) platform survive today but those on the up side disappeared in the 1920s rebuilding to four tracks. (*Larry Morgan*). *Below:* Liverpool Street station in the early 1950s with motive power much the same as during the author's time here as an Assistant to the Divisional Locomotive Running Superintendent. (*Kenneth Field*).

Above: The author with pupils in the Instruction Train. Here he demonstrates the finer points of valve gear. *Below:* A general view of the demonstration items in the Instruction Train. Some of the equipment is full size but with cutaway sections to show interiors, while other features are illustrated by models, most of which are now in the National Railway Museum at York.

5 That half an hour should elapse between the starting of trains from the same station.

6 All carriages should be fitted with spring buffers.

7 All engines should have six wheels.

8 Every railway line to be marked with mile posts 'so that every passenger, so disposed, may have an opportunity of checking the rate of travel'. (Thomson does not say what the passengers should do in the event of the speed becoming excessive!)

9 That the chairs of the ECR 'were much too slight'.

As soon as the Smith and Thomson Reports became available, revealing the shortcomings that caused the accidents and recommending measures to prevent recurrence, the value of investigations into such incidents by independent inspectors at once became apparent. Not all of the nine Thomson recommendations were adopted there and then but, apart from No 4 which was rather pointless, they all came into effect in one way or another eventually; No 5 appears to have been the birth of the Time Interval System by which many railways came to be operated for the next 30 to 40 years, until Block Working superseded it.

All the Reports written in and since 1840 by the RI's Officers on railway accidents have been published, and proposals for improvements which they have suggested have always been in the form of recommendations; enactments on the operation of railways have been applied sparingly and only when proposals and advice have failed to achieve what the RI has considered necessary. This method of approach is universally accepted nowadays as having been the best; persuasion and co-operation have avoided a mass of legislation such as that which confronts modern motor car drivers and brings hundreds of them to the courts every day. Only on the very few occasions when certain standards have had to be introduced for all railways to follow, or when there was a need for safety measures that directors were disinclined to adopt on account of cost, has compulsion by law been introduced, as Acts of Parliament or Statutory Orders.

The whole aim of the RI's accident investigation procedure is to be helpful, by finding out in each case what has gone wrong and, in cooperation with the railway management, to devise improvements which will ensure that the kind of accident that has happened will not occur again. Identifying someone as the man who was to blame and putting him in a pillory is not the primary purpose of an Inquiry into a railway accident, although, of course, if it is clear that a man did make a mistake or by lapsing in some way allowed the accident to happen the Report has to say so.

For the RI's first 30 years its inspectors held accident Inquiries without any statutory powers to do so; the railways co-operated and that was deemed sufficient. After a review in 1870, however, the 1871 Railway Regulation Act was passed, providing powers that are still in force today. The rights under this Act are extensive; an inspector directed to hold an Inquiry may enter the railway's premises for the purpose, scrutinise any papers, records or documents that he requires to see, examine any lines or rolling stock, and interview any of the railway's employees who are compelled to answer every question that he may put to them. The Act also makes it obligatory for the inspector to submit a Report on his findings which is for the information of the Secretary of State or the Minister but is addressed to his Permanent Secretary.

As late as 1889, however, trains were still, on some lines, being run without positive arrangements to guard against collision. Stations and junctions had signals but block signalling was not yet universal and many routes continued to be operated by the Time Interval System; after a train had left a station a following train was detained until a prescribed minimum period had elapsed. The period might be ten minutes, it being expected that by then the first train would be perhaps five or six miles ahead, or would be protected by detonators and hand signals should it have stopped or been delayed en route. There were also many passenger trains lacking automatic brakes or indeed any form of power brake on the carriages at all. A brake that acts on a train from end to end, or at least on most of the carriages including the last, and arranged so that all the brake cylinders can be worked by the driver on the footplate, is called a continuous brake. An automatic brake is one designed so that if some of the carriages become detached from the rest the brake will at once apply fully on both portions, without anyone being able to withhold its action.

Although by 1889 the RI had already, and frequently, advocated block working on all passenger lines and the automatic brake on every passenger train, railway directors were not hurrying to comply; they had to pay shareholders' dividends if they hoped for retention on their Boards and when earnings allowed only for safety provisions *or* dividends they met their dilemma by declaring block working and automatic brakes to be luxuries and quite unnecessary for the railways that they controlled. The RI lacked powers to compel the adoption of these two safety essentials and Parliament remained unconvinced that enforcement was necessary, until 12 June 1889, the day of the appalling runaway collision on the Armagh – Goraghwood line of the Great Northern Railway (Ireland).

The line was single and worked by staff and ticket on a ten minute time interval principle. At 10.15am an excursion train of 15 carriages, having a 'simple' non-automatic vacuum brake, left Armagh with nearly 1,000 passengers but the engine, No 86, was unable to get its load up a 1 in 75 gradient and the train stuck some 200yd from the summit, known as Dobbin's Bridge. The trainmen decided they would take the first five carriages to a siding further on, at Hamilton's Bawn, and then come back with the engine for the rest but when the rear ten carriages had been detached they began to run back, overcoming the one hand brake and a few stones put hopefully on the rails as security. They careered about a mile and a half at increasing speed until they collided end on with the following regular passenger train which had left Armagh at 10.38am; the excursion train's three rear carriages were completely destroyed when they struck the locomotive (No 9) of the 10.38 train which was turned upside down by the impact; 80 people were killed, including 20 children, and 260 injured.

Had block working been in force the second train could not have left Armagh while the excursion train still occupied the section ahead although this would probably not have made much difference; had the line been clear the runaway portion would have travelled all the way to Armagh and probably met its end there instead of where it did. The want of an automatic brake was the crucial matter; carriages equipped with it would not have run back. Both these aspects were righted once and for all by a Regulation of Railways Bill which was laid before Parliament almost immediately after the accident; on becoming law it gave the BOT powers to order the adoption of the absolute block system and also of the automatic brake for all passenger carrying vehicles, and the BOT made its Order at the same time. It was left to the railways, however, to select the best type of brake to employ and unfortunately they did not all choose the same, some already having adopted the vacuum brake and others the Westinghouse compressed air type, an inconsistency that compelled many companies to provide 'dual fitted' rolling stock for through running.

In 1900 another Act appeared called The Railway Employment (Prevention of Accidents) Act; the mysterious appended code, '63 & 64 Vict Ch 27' means that it became law in the 63rd/64th year of Queen Victoria's reign and occurs in Chapter 27 of that year's Statute Book, all Acts being numbered successively as Chapters each year. This Act authorised the BOT to make Rules on certain aspects of railway working; the first set of Rules was issued in 1902, making a number of practices compulsory and prohibiting others, for the greater safety of railway workers, and it is still binding by law today, just as an Act of Parliament is. The Rules must not be confused with the contents of the railways' own rule books, although some of the railway rules virtually copy the Statutory Rules. There are nine Rules in the 1902 set and they are, briefly, as follows:

1 Wagons must, in general, have destination labels on both sides (so that traffic staff can read them without any need to cross the track).

2 Wagons must not be moved by means of a prop or pole, or towed by a rope or chain attached to a locomotive or vehicle on an adjacent line, except 'where no other reasonably practicable means can be provided for dealing with the traffic'. (The railways themselves extended this to wagon towing by road motors).

3 Engines and tenders must have power brakes in addition to hand brakes, except engines used solely for shunting, provided that they have sufficiently powerful hand brakes.

4 Places where shunting is frequent after dark must be sufficiently lighted.

5 Point rods and signal wires positioned where they would be a source of danger to employees must be covered or guarded and ground levers for points must be installed so that men working them are clear of the line, and in general they must be parallel to the line.

6 Water gauge glasses on both locomotive and stationary boilers must be covered by protectors.

7 Tool and equipment boxes on engines must be arranged so that men can get to them without undue risk of injury when their engine is in motion; locomotive water tanks must have water level gauges readable from the footplate.

8 Trains working outside station limits must have brake vans 'or other suitable vehicles' for the guard.

9 Lookout protection, in the form of lookoutmen or 'apparatus', must be provided for men working on the permanent way when any danger is likely to arise, to warn them of oncoming trains.

There was another Rule in 1911; it laid down that all wagons must have hand brake levers on each side, and specified the lever arrangement that is to be seen on every ordinary goods wagon today. Wagons of over 20 tons capacity are exempt from the need for levers and more often than not have hand wheels and screws.

Despite all the legislation and the care that is taken to keep it up to date by revision, things now and then get overlooked by both the RI and the railways themselves, an entertaining example having been connected with the Railway Clauses Act of 1845. Section 48 lays down that 'where the railway crosses any turnpike road on the level adjoining to a station, all trains on the railway shall be made to slacken their speed before arriving at such turnpike road, and shall not cross the same at any greater rate than four miles an hour'. Whether the clause became forgotten as railways developed and as the years went by, or whether it was concluded that as soon as turnpikes disappeared this remarkable restriction on speed no longer applied I do not know; shortly after 1930, however, it seems to have been decided that the limitation was unrealistic and the words from 'all trains' to 'an hour' were repealed by the Road & Rail Traffic Act of 1933. As this was about the time that the LNER was developing its pioneer high speed trains it was as well that Section 48 was not raised by some crackpot or other before the repeal became law.

8 First Years in the Inspectorate

On joining the RI my first task was to learn the work. The IOs' duties are in the main twofold; one is the inspection of new lines or of major alterations to existing lines and the other is the investigation of accidents involving trains and particularly passenger trains. The EIs investigate accidents to railway personnel, such as shunting mishaps, cases of men getting run down by trains while repairing the permanent way, and instances of men being struck by trains or shunting movements when going about the tracks in the course of ordinary duty. These three categories are by no means all, and of nearly 1,000 accidents that I alone have investigated hardly two have been alike.

All accidents to passengers, and all accidents to railway staff, either fatal or that have prevented them from earning full wages for more than three days, and the accident causes must, under the 1871 Act, be reported to the RI by the railways; the accident forms are scrutinised either by an IO or, in the case of personnel accidents, by the Senior EI. The papers on accidents into which it is decided that an Inquiry should be held are then set aside. All fatalities must be reported to the RI promptly by telegraph or telephone, followed by returns as soon as possible. All this was new to me when I first arrived at the MOT&CA; I knew next to nothing of the work that I was going to have to do, and there was much to learn.

The Senior EI was Mr J.L.M. Moore, of South Eastern & Chatham Railway origin; Mr R.H. Williams, an ex LMS man, was the oldest of the EIs and in due course succeeded Mr Moore. I was aware at the outset that my duties were going to involve a considerable amount of travelling and so it proved; an EI's normal output was two Inquiries and two Reports a week, which does not sound very much to someone who has never tried it. It meant that in a week an inspector had to plan and arrange two Inquiries, travel to the places concerned, conduct the Inquiries, come back, write the Reports, get them typed and sign them, all in $5\frac{1}{2}$ days, for we worked on Saturday mornings at that time; the places to be visited might well be in Devon or Midlothian. A personnel accident Inquiry was and still is held in the manner of an extremely informal court; the Inspector visits the accident site, or examines the machine or equipment that has been involved, sometimes taking witnesses with him to demonstrate what went wrong, and then he interviews each witness, either in an office or sometimes in the open, taking notes of the evidence. Thus if the accident is one in which some luggage vans have run out of control along a siding and collided with a sleeping car, overbalancing a few cleaners at work inside the vehicle, the Inspector would need to see the siding where the incident happened, noting any gradients or curves, and then he would require to hear the accounts of the accident given by the cleaners, the shunters who had been in charge of the vans, the man who reversed the points concerned or failed to reverse them as the case might be, the driver of the locomotive that moved the vans initially, and perhaps the supervisor of the work normally carried out in the siding who would probably be a yardmaster or a station manager. When all the evidence has been gathered the case is then discussed with the local railway officers, after which the Inspector leaves and begins his writing.

The art of holding such an investigation is to put each witness completely at ease, express sympathy whenever appropriate if the incident has been one of death or serious injury, and persuade him to talk. The Inspector must keep his own mouth shut and his ears wide open, and he must bear in mind that men whose ordinary work is almost entirely out of doors may be feeling a little in awe of a room full of people. Most men prefer to give their evidence by talking in their own way; very rarely does a witness ever attempt to say anything but the truth, although if men anticipate that any blame appears to be coming their way they will, very naturally, try to ward if off! It is far better to gather evidence in this manner than to play at 'solicitors' or 'learned counsel' and to attempt by cunning interrogation to trap the witnesses and get them into corners, as the professionals do in the courts. Officers of the railwaymen's Trade Unions are invariably present at Inquiries and these men, all of them experienced railwaymen themselves and who work hard on behalf of their members, giving long hours of service to the Union that employs them, never fail to take a common sense view of every accident, help the witnesses to relax and to have no fear of the Inquiry proceedings, and very often offer the Inspector good advice.

Writing the Report is the Inspector's most difficult task. To those who have never yet attempted it, the production of an accident Report on, perhaps, two sheets of A4 paper might appear to be easy and everyone who joins the team of EIs invariably thinks so. In fact, it takes years of pen work before an Inspector becomes competent to produce a good, concise and accurate account of an accident, leaving out all unnecessary or irrelevant details; I was fortunate to have Mr Moore and then Mr Williams to train me and I remain grateful for all time to these two men who taught me everything they could before I myself took over the senior position.

Every Report becomes a public document once it is issued and almost all those on train accidents are printed and published by Her Majesty's Stationery Office, from where they can be purchased; most of the EIs Reports are photo-copied and then distributed free to the railways and to anyone who asks for them. Until about 1950 the arrangements for circulating EIs' Reports were very limited; the Ministry gave them to the railways' General Managers but the ordinary supervisors and their men never received them and remained ignorant of the contents and recommendations, if indeed they ever heard that Reports had been written. All this was changed, however, when British Railways set up its Accident Prevention Service and nowadays the Reports are copied and widely distributed by the Service's officers. Nevertheless, the lack of requirements that the Inspectors' Reports shall be distributed to men in need of the lessons that most Reports convey remains a weakness of the 1871 Act.

HM Stationery Office is the Government publisher, producing the *London Gazette, Hansard,* all the Acts of Parliament and numerous pamphlets and booklets. 'Government Publications' may sound decidedly dull and unattractive to many people but my advice to anyone who hasn't yet done so is to visit one of the HMSO Bookshops where splendid books on archaeology, science, industry and art, to mention only a few topics, are available.

I began my new work by attending about a dozen Inquiries held by the other EIs. Train accident Inquiries held by the IOs are conducted in public, and EIs' Inquiries into accidents that have occurred to railway staff are *deemed* to be held in public, that is to say, anyone may attend the proceedings and listen to the evidence. There is, however, no legal requirement that the Ministry shall publish notices in advance to say that an Inquiry will be taking place. The Senior EI suggests for Inquiry all the cases that he feels should be investigated; if the Minister or his authorised officer agrees, which he invariably does, he issues an Order for an EI to hold an Inquiry into each incident, the principle being that an accident's circumstances should be examined if it appears that improvement is needed in some direction or other. It is then the Inspector's task to find out what went amiss, resulting in the accident, and to recommend measures if he can that should prevent such an incident from happening again.

I learned that all personnel accidents on the railways are attributable to one of five possible causes, or occasionally to two or more of them. These causes are: 1) the fault of the man or men who became victims of the accident, 2) someone else's fault, 3) defective equipment or materials, 4) defective working practices, and 5) miscellaneous, which is a bin where all the uncertain cases are dropped. Accidents to men who suddenly become faint or ill and fall as a result in front of a train or from ladders or signal posts are regarded as 'miscellaneous'. As a rule, Inquiries are held into all fatalities, whether preventive measures seem possible or not; suicide or trespass cases are not investigated by the RI, however, as it is quite purposeless to follow up accidents to people who have gone onto the lines or onto any other part of the railway deliberately and illegally for reasons of their own. As well as railway employees, 'persons on business' come within the scope of an EI's work, these being people such as coal merchants or scrap metal dealers who work in railway goods yards, employees of contractors who have been engaged by a National or Local Authority to lay cables, water pipes or drains over or beneath the line, or Post Office staff who have duties at stations.

Early in 1954 I held my first Inquiry. The case was simple although I am sorry to say that it involved a fatality; an unfortunate engine driver who had begun to step over a main line was taken unawares by a train because in a few moments of inattention to his safety he had forgotten first to look along the tracks. I had to realise at the outset of my new career that the tragedy of death and injury was going to feature continuously in my duties but that at the same time there was a worthwhile object before me which was the reduction of sad and unnecessary wastage of manpower. I hope that in my 25 years in the RI I have contributed at least something towards this end.

Having held the Inquiry the next thing was to write the Report. The way an accident Report is presented is, briefly, to open it with an introductory paragraph that tells in a sentence or two what happened, then to follow with descriptive matter, the evidence, conclusions and findings, ending with any recommendations and remarks. The Report must be simple and easy to read but commonplace railway jargon or slang is not permitted. A driver does not 'learn the road' – he arranges a journey in order to become acquainted with it; he does not 'fill the tank' – he replenishes the locomotive or tender tank with water. A shunter does not 'wave a red lamp' or 'pull points over' – he exhibits a handsignal with a lamp showing a red light and he reverses the points. The 'board' isn't 'off' – the signal shows a clear aspect; the signalman does not 'put a lever back' – he restores it to its normal position. Eventually I finished my first draft, very excellently written and ready for issue; I then let Mr Moore read it and was mortified to see it heavily amended, for he had had 30 years' experience of report writing and knew his work very thoroughly indeed. Under his guidance my Report was soon licked into shape.

I was given further Inquiries to conduct, a few at a time to begin with. I had, of course, until I left the railway service, kept a watch on the staff vacancy lists that were circulated, applying for posts for which I felt qualified and sometimes getting interviews. It was rather startling, therefore, to find occasionally when opening my Inquiries that the Departmental railway officers who attended so that they could assist by producing plans, records and rule books were men who had recently interviewed me for positions that they needed to fill, had questioned me closely on my capabilities and had then appointed someone else! They appreciated, of course, that in my new capacity I was merely doing my duty when, instead, they had to answer questions put by me and we both tactfully avoided references to the past.

Mr Moore showed me how to handle paper work that was additional to producing accident Reports. One task was the perusal of letters that came from the public on every conceivable railway aspect; there were complaints about train services, engine smoke, noise caused by men repairing the tracks at night, bad delays, uncomfortable carriages and the opening times of refreshment rooms. There were (and still are) details of crackbrain inventions, or approaches from salesmen trying to get the Ministry to interest railway managers in articles of commerce they were endeavouring to market. All such communications were eventually passed to the railways concerned; only if safety was in question did the RI take any action.

Every Government Department receives huge amounts of correspondence and many thousands of letters arrived at the MOT&CA daily. Private letters were taken by messengers to the individuals to whom they were addressed and all others were opened by a team of girls who identified the contents of the envelopes and passed them to the appropriate Divisions, no easy task in the case of a rambling letter running to six sheets of paper with an opening paragraph that bewailed overcrowding at Oxford Circus Underground station at 5.0pm on weekdays and final lines offering good advice on the running of motor coaches in the Scottish Highlands. People would do well to realise that it is quite futile to write to a Government Department unless there is proper and specific business to conduct. It seems to be imagined by some that if they write personally to a Minister, airing grievances, giving him sound counsel or expressing political views, their letter will, on receipt, at once be laid on his desk and that he will there and then push all his other work aside and give it his exclusive attention. In fact, a letter of that kind goes to a suitable Division and a clerical officer replies to the effect that the Minister has specially appointed him to attend to the matter and is deeply grateful for the interest that has been shown. Unannounced and unexpected visitors who arrive at a Ministry, waving papers and demanding to be conducted to the Minister's room at once, are placated in much the same way.

Indeed, a Minister himself normally deals only with correspondence written or forwarded to him by a Member of Parliament, and with documents of such high importance that they can be manipulated only at Ministerial level.

Crazy inventions are offered to almost all Ministries having technical Divisions; the RI certainly gets its share. A favourite theme is monorail development; self appointed experts seem to imagine that by having all new lines laid as monorail systems, or existing railways converted to monorail working, present day operating difficulties would immediately be overcome and vanish for ever. Some monorail designs are at least 100 years old and their proprietors make periodic claims that their systems permit great speeds quite unattainable on an orthodox railway, although such an argument must by now be getting a little weak in the face of modern high speed development. The simplest answer to everyone obsessed with monorail ideas is that no one has yet invented a suitable and safe set of points by which a monorail vehicle can be readily diverted from one track to another; all that the designers have produced so far are clumsy devices that involve shifting a length of the entire railway formation. Moreover, if monorails had the claimed advantages over conventional railways we should now have a countrywide monorail network instead of duorails.

The Wuppertal Suspension Railway (Schwebebahn), worked by cars suspended from a track carried by overhead structures, is one of the few existing successful monorail systems, having been in regular operation since 1901, but it consists only of a double line route eight miles in length with a turning loop at each end to avoid the need for crossover points. The Lartigue system that once operated between Listowel and Ballybunion was moderately effective; the track was a single rail carried about 3ft 6in above the ground by steel trestles standing at 3ft 3in intervals, and the rolling stock was in 'pannier' form, hanging down on each side of the rail, each locomotive having two boilers. Opened in 1888, it worked a regular passenger and goods service but, situated in a remote part of County Kerry, it never paid its way and closed in 1924. Today, had it survived, managed by a preservation society in a well-populated area, such a railway would be a roaring success.

Track design provides further openings for the fanciful inventor. Memorials are delivered to the RI depicting wonderful new ways of making rail joints, the initiators completely overlooking the fact that the fishplate has long since proved itself to be the most effective way of fastening rails to one another, bettered only by the modern system of continuous welding.

Many of the 'new' proposed devices are merely forms of joint chair, similar to those that the fishplate superseded. Then there are the signalling inventions and in this sphere drawings and specifications are offered to the RI by the dozen, depicting astonishing arrangements of wires, levers, wheels, pulleys, lights, bells and batteries, intended for reasons that are generally vague to replace already well-established signalling methods. All inventors who proffer their ideas are always properly thanked for their interest in railway affairs; their papers are usually passed to the BRB, the originators being told that this has been done and that the railway officers will doubtless read them attentively. I suppose these instigators mean well.

I was soon travelling all over the country, producing about two Reports a week. Most of the cases that I investigated during my first year or two were routine incidents of the kind that have been occurring ever since railways began, such as shunters sustaining injuries when coupling or detaching coaches or wagons, men falling off locomotives or guards' vans, other men getting knocked down on the line or in sidings by shunting movements, or permanent way staff being run down by trains which they or their lookoutmen ought to have seen in time. Steam locomotives were still working most of the trains at this period and I had more than one Inquiry to hold into accidents and sometimes tragedies which had resulted from attempts by unqualified men to work the controls of locomotives within motive power depots.

It is sheer folly for anyone other than a qualified driver to attempt to move an engine in steam and indeed a wicked crime; it frequently happens that, with the regulator having been opened, the engine starts but then gets out of control; it may then collide with other engines, fall into a turntable pit or enter a dead-ended shed and knock out the wall at the far end, maybe bringing the roof down as well. The culprits were usually fitters' mates, young engine cleaners, or shed staff such as coalmen or ashpit clearers who thought they could safely move an inconvenient engine just a few yards on their own to get it out of the way, instead of asking a driver to do it for them. They often overlooked that in the case of a superheated engine, once the regulator is opened the whole superheater fills with steam under pressure before the wheels begin to move; after reclosing the regulator there is then still enough steam in the superheater elements to turn the engine's driving wheels three or four revolutions.

Every railway accident Report is put onto the file to which the case belongs and never leaves it; the Reports that are distributed are copies of the originals. The files are kept for a certain number of years and then destroyed, unless some of the papers that they contain need to be preserved for reasons of policy or precedent. A few copies of each Report are, however, bound into volumes to be kept for perpetuity.

The Ministry's filing system for papers was, I found, pretty well infallible. A file was opened for every new accident case that was going to be the subject of Inquiry, and there were also files for all the other features on which the RI was continuously taking action. A Registry issued each file to begin with and recorded the individual to whom it was sent; if that person passed the file to somebody else he had to enter on a 'charge slip' the details of the file's move. The slip went to the Registry staff who adjusted their records, and if a certain file was required they could say immediately who had it. So no one could dodge a difficult task by just letting the file get lost, as I once did with a huge batch of engine casualty forms at Gateshead; if a man had a file the Registry people were aware of it and he was responsible for that file until he passed it into someone else's possession. Files no longer needed in the offices were put away in the Registry's filing rooms, huge places with shelf spaces for thousands of files that were always readily available at a moment's notice.

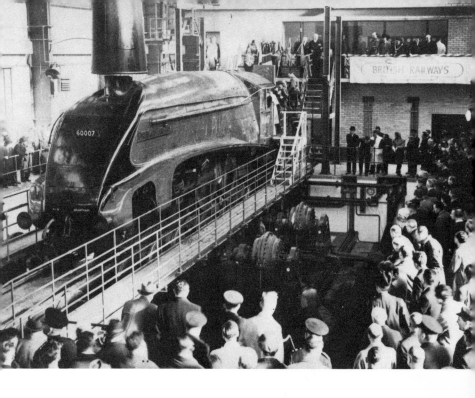

Above: The Rugby Locomotive Testing Station opening day celebrations, during which A4 4–6–2 No 60007 demonstrated the new test equipment to Ministry of Transport and BTC guests and the press. (*National Railway Museum*). *Below:* Among the several types tested at Rugby was Gresley D49 4–4–0 No 62764. (*J. M. Jarvis*).

Left: The Tay Bridge from the southern side. The piers of the ill-fated Bouch bridge are on the right of the present structure. *Below:* Beneath the Tay Bridge deck. The outer girders are from the old bridge, dismantled after the 1879 disaster. The permanent walkway for maintenance staff runs down the centre of the bridge, to the left of the main girders seen here. Examination and painting of the outer girders needs the use of duckboards. There have been occasional fatalities when men have fallen into the river as related by the author on page 156.

9 Senior Railway Employment Inspector

Mr Moore retired in 1954; Mr Williams who succeeded him retired in January 1958 and on the 27th of that month I took the Senior Employment Inspector's position, a post that I was to occupy for 17 years. Within a year or two all the EI positions became vacant; I had to supervise new men who filled them but, all four of us still being fairly young and of similar ages, we formed a congenial and enthusiastic team with up to date knowledge of railway affairs and unhampered by the traditions that seemed to some extent to have beset the older men whose places we had taken.

One of my many new tasks as the SEI was to prepare a part of the CIO's Annual Report. This Report, now known as the *Safety Record of the Railways in Great Britain* which is a far better title because the very name 'Annual Report' is enough to dispirit most people, whatever its topic, is not a document required by statute, as are the accident Reports; nevertheless, a comprehensive summary of each year's work is deemed necessary and most Government Departments produce some form of annual account of their stewardships. The writing of the Safety Record takes two to three months, each IO and the SEI drafting his share of the work while clerical officers are assembling its statistics and tables. The work cannot be started until the spring because it takes at least two months at the start of each year to collect the data from the railways for the final months of the year before, and then when the Record is finished it still has to be printed and its proofs checked before it can be issued. My part of the Record amounted, year by year, to several pages summing up the railway personnel accidents; my first contribution, to the 1957 Record, was rather crude but I believe I improved as the years proceeded.

On 20 March 1958 Lt-Col Wilson died suddenly. He had left his office in Berkeley Square House at about midday and shortly after lunch he was taken ill, collapsing a few hours later. I may well have been the last person to whom he spoke by telephone; I was at home for a few days, looking after the house and my five year old daughter as my wife was ill in bed. On the morning of the 20th he received a note from me, explaining my absence from duty, and he telephoned just before noon, expressing sympathy and very generously telling me not to attempt to return until my wife had made a proper recovery; I was never to hear his voice again. His place was taken by Brigadier C.A. Langley.

Early in 1958 I made a silly mistake in an accident Report that landed me in a Crown Court witness box. It has always been an RI principle that investigations and findings are not for the purpose of assisting civil claims for damages or compensation; the Inspectorate's Inquiry work is for the sole purpose of discovering accident causes with a view to devising means of preventing recurrence. Firms of solicitors about to start civil proceedings often apply for copies of inspectors' Reports and are, of course, entitled to have them, and they are at perfect liberty to use them in court if they wish; the Reports are public documents. But for an Inspector to have to attend court is another matter; Inspectors' investigations are not made for the purpose of assisting civil proceedings and it is considered that people who are starting litigation must seek their evidence elsewhere.

I shall not reveal the place or details of this accident but it involved the proper use of a railway regulation that was somewhat ambiguous, but at the same time difficult to word in any other way, having regard to the circumstances with which it dealt. Whether or not the railway was responsible for the accident appeared to depend on the meaning of one or two words and instead of writing in my Report that the regulation was uncertain in its interpretation I more or less said what I believed the meaning to be, which was a thoughtless thing to do because it is for British Railways to interpret their own Rules, not for a Government Department. Solicitors acting for a claimant seized on my slip and in due course a horrid slouching character arrived at Berkeley Square House to hand me a subpoena which was a summons to attend the Courts of Justice. I could have thrown it out of the window there and then because the learned solicitors had forgotten first to take it to the Court to get it signed but that would have merely caused another summons to arrive, properly prepared.

So to court I had to go and was made to confirm my elucidation of the rule but I did my best to make it clear that I occupied the witness box only under protest and was embarrassed by having to give evidence against British Railways when, acting in a semi-judicial capacity, I had investigated the case myself, with powers probably greater than those of the Judge, having been able to ask questions unhampered by 'rules of evidence', whatever *they* are, and when I had received much help and ready co-operation from every railway officer and man concerned. The Judge gave me a rather reproving lecture on his side of the business, which was the dispensation of justice; we parted, each retaining his own views. I learned a little, however, of how to face counsel and I have been taken to a few civil courts since, where I learned more.

No court has powers to demand of a witness that he forms an opinion, although if he is asked for an opinion that he already holds he must then state it. At one of my court appearances a cross examining counsel, instead of asking me a question, 'suggested that something or other was actually the case' but I told him that I hadn't any comments to make on his suggestion, for a court does not have powers to make a witness enter into discussion. At one court a plaintiff's advocate put me in the witness box as an 'expert witness', that is to say, one who has special knowledge or skill; to introduce me to the Court as such but afraid, perhaps, that I might be evasive and deny any such talents, he said in a very low voice 'I take it that you are an expert on railway rules', at the same time rearranging a few books, presumably by way of distraction. Had I said 'yes' my status as an expert would then have been established, but fortunately thoughts came quickly and I told him that this was something that I had never considered, putting him in a dilemma for a few moments. Anyone who is looking for an expert witness in a case against British Railways is, of course, in difficulties; all the experts are in the service of British Railways! One barrister I recollect who, on getting a remark from me that did not suit him at all, asked 'are you trying to be clever?'; I told him 'no, it just comes naturally!' I enjoyed that moment.

Although people who are handed subpoenas are usually asked at the same time by the process servers for details such as full names, home addresses, ages, qualifications and so on, there are no powers to support such demands. Servers handing me subpoenas get nothing in return except directions to depart; no one can be made to say anything at all until he is in the witness box and has taken the oath, and indeed no information should be imparted except, in fairness, to both sides simultaneously.

Now and then solicitors attend accident Inquiries, usually to represent a man who, having sustained injury in the incident, hopes to make a civil claim for compensation; in most cases they are content to sit quietly and to hear the account of what has occurred, the Inspector not allowing them to turn his Inquiry into a court for determination of liability. At Inquests I have seen solicitors or counsel examining witnesses and learned a few of the legal man's ways of attempting to influence a court if things are looking bad for his client. One is to cause a witness to say things that are absolutely irrelevant to the case in hand and then expound on them at length to divert attention from evidence that really matters. I have had to watch out for this when holding Inquiries with solicitors present; it is usual to allow them to put questions to witnesses although only out of courtesy because at the Inquiry they have no status at all, but any attempt to introduce features not having a bearing on the case must be slapped down. Thus, in an instance of a man on the line being struck by a train, it is of no consequence at all to the Inspector whether the train was running early, on time or late, and of no significance if the driver happened to be newly qualified and had never worked a train on his own responsibility before. Even a solicitor takes his first court case, never having conducted one previously.

One of the 1871 Act's Sections provides that a Coroner in England may request the RI to provide the services of an assessor to assist him at an Inquest on any person killed on a railway. I have acted several times as a Coroner's assessor but I am surprised that more Coroners do not avail themselves of the facility, which costs them nothing. The assessor's duty is to help the Coroner and his jury by explaining railway rules, technical terms and describing railway apparatus, but a good many Coroners, especially those in small towns and rural places, tend to be sufficiently pleased with their own capabilities to consider that they can manage on their own, and take advantage of the spotlight of publicity that is upon them at their Inquests by airing their knowledge, being disinclined, it seems, to be seen with an assessor sitting alongside them on their benches.

For some reason the Act excludes Wales but the RI has always, on request, assisted Welsh Coroners and Scottish Procurators Fiscal in the same way, nevertheless.

My first experience as an assessor was at Longtown when the Coroner for the Eastern Division of Cumberland held an Inquest on 27 May 1960. I had already had an Inquiry into the accident which was a particularly unfortunate one that had occurred on a three mile single line branch that ran from Longtown, on the Carlisle to Edinburgh line, to Gretna on the Glasgow main line. A locomotive was propelling a single goods van with a 20 ton brake van in front of it when, on nearing Gretna, the brake van became derailed and toppled over; the guard either fell or jumped from the van and was killed when the overturning vehicle trapped him. Employees of an engineering firm had made a level crossing of their own over the branch so that lorries could move spoil to their work site; flangeways that they had formed by laying timber between the rails had soon become choked with soil and gravel spilled by the lorries as they bumped over the track and it was this blockage that brought about the derailment. It was a serious mistake by the firm's men to make gaps in the railway fences and to put down a crossing but they doubtless knew that the track, which looked more like a minor siding than a branch connected to two main lines, was infrequently used and I am sure that they did not realise the wrong that they were doing. Although the permanent way ganger had noticed the crossing during his patrols he had assumed that it must have been made with proper authority.

The Coroner was a Carlisle solicitor; he was, I believe, in his eighties and not very steady on his feet but mentally he was very alert indeed, as I rapidly found out when I let my attention on the Inquest proceedings wander a few moments and was pulled up sharply by 'Mr Hewison, do you not agree with what I have just said?'! However, I gave his jury all the help they needed with regard to rolling stock, permanent way, railway rules and the Act that provided for railway fencing, and a verdict of 'accidentally killed' was returned. In addition to the Report that I wrote on my own investigations I had to comply with the 1871 Act by submitting another on the Inquest but it was very brief as such Inquest Reports invariably are, there being no point in setting out all the details twice.

On 31 January 1963 Brigadier Langley retired from the post of CIO of Railways, being succeeded by Col Denis McMullen, the third CIO under whom I was to work. Col J.H. Robertson followed him in January 1969 and in January 1974 Lt-Col I.K.A. McNaughton became the CIO.

By the spring of 1961 the Ministry, which had changed its name from MOT&CA to MOT on 14 October 1959, had been moved from Berkeley Square to a newly-built office block appropriately named St Christopher House, in Southwark. The RI took only its documents; all the furniture was left behind which was just as well as there had hardly been any renewals since World War I and it was getting very dilapidated, although Lt-Col Wilson had been rather proud of a chair in his room that, he declared, had belonged to the first Inspector General of Railways. The rooms into which we moved were already equipped for us with modern new furniture and we found the accommodation excellent.

On 15 October 1970 the MOT was merged with the Ministry of Housing & Local Government and the Ministry of Town & Country Planning to form the Department of the Environment with three Ministers, one of whom covered Transport Industries. This was followed up by moving again in August 1971 to yet another brand new building, at No 2 Marsham Street in Westminster and only a few hundred yards from the Houses of Parliament. Once more we were transferred to rooms pre-furnished with new office equipment that, we were led to believe, was of the Government's latest design. The RI was put on the 18th floor of one of the building's towers, giving us in summer a glorious view across the whole of London. RI staff were not very impressed by the furniture and most of us managed to get our previous desks and bookcases smuggled across from Southwark. From the 18th floor we could see the building in Cowley Street that was once the London office of the North Eastern Railway; British Railways no longer owns it but a glance shows it to be a small replica of the great NER headquarters building in York. The DOE kept the RI until 8 November 1976 when all the transport Divisions were taken from it and became the Department of Transport; the huge building that houses the two Departments has never been named and remains 'No 2 Marsham Street'.

Early in the 1960s the British Railways Board (BRB) began to consider rewriting the railway Rule Book and the RI took the opportunity to suggest that the time had come for a very drastic revision indeed. The Rule Book then in force had been issued in 1950, its form more or less following the rule books that had been distributed by the railway companies during the previous century; no one within the last hundred years had been

149

sufficiently bold to do more than to add odd pieces here and there to cover new operating situations that arose. It had become a hotchpotch of regulations, some of which were quite out of date or were hardly rules at all but merely commercial requirements. Rule 17, for example, laid down that stationmasters were responsible for the cleanliness of station lavatories which were to be inspected daily, and for the proper and economic use of stores; Rule 30 required that when a shunting horse at work on the railway was about to be passed by a train a man had to hold its head although it did not say from where the man was to appear for the purpose, and Rule 33 said that station clocks 'must be corrected as may be necessary'. Engineering Department methods for taking possession of one track and leaving trains to run under single line working conditions on the other were specified in the Rule Book but the manner of taking possession when single line working was not required was set out in the General Appendix. The Rule Book stipulated that a handsignalman had first to be passed as proficient if he was required to protect a ballast train being loaded or unloaded but did not require him to be so qualified for any other handsignalman's duties. Rule 71, with its reference to 'boys', had apparently been written before education for children became compulsory.

Rewriting began in or about 1965 and as the draft of each section was finished the BRB sent it to the RI for comment and review; when we had studied it we had a meeting with the Board's officers concerned, at which we suggested improvements and I gave guidance on the aspects of staff safety. It was about 1970 before all the editing was complete; the new Rule Book was issued to railway staff on 1 October 1972. It must not be thought, however, that the Rule Book as it stands today was the work of the Department of Transport; the RI only offered advice, and the final form of each rule was decided on entirely by the BRB, whose rules they were.

The mechanics of clocks is one of my delights and it was thanks to studies in this direction that I was able to solve a perplexing accident that happened in Yorkshire in 1961 when a crane jib suddenly dropped, fatally injuring a man. The crane was lifting track sections when the jib derricking rope suddenly gave way. The rope was a steel wire cable half an inch in diameter and 218ft in length, and had broken 60ft 6in from the end that was attached to the derricking drum. When a wire rope breaks it has either been overloaded until every strand has been pulled apart by the tension or else it has been severed by a bruising or chopping action. A momentary inspection of the broken strands, better studied through a magnifying glass, reveals the cause; a slight drawing out of each strand at its broken end indicates overloading, and a flattening or shearing shows that the rope was crushed. I soon saw that this particular jib rope had been initially damaged by crushing; the question before me was how did it happen.

An ordinary eight day or 'grandfather' clock has two weights each of ten to twelve pounds hanging from a strong gut cord known as a *line* and the winding up process coils the line onto a drum or barrel about $2\frac{1}{4}$in in diameter. The clock's normal working allows the barrel to let out its line at the rate of one revolution every twelve hours and when the weight has completely run down, at the end of eight days, it takes 16 turns of the key or handle to re-wind it fully. The barrel is grooved to accommodate 16 coils of line plus a small margin, but no more; when a new line is fitted it must be cut to a length which just fills the barrel for if it is too long the barrel will be full before the weight arrives at the top and further winding will cause the line to ride over its previous coils and perhaps wander onto and jam the adjacent gear wheel.

The crane's derricking gear had a barrel similar to that of a clock but about seven inches in diameter; there was a flange at one end but at the other there was a worm wheel, which is a gear wheel driven by a revolving worm screw, and this wheel acted as the opposite flange. The crane's makers specified a jib rope length of 205ft for the type of crane concerned and I found by calculation that with such a rope the barrel was nicely filled when the jib was in its uppermost position. The fitter who had put on the 218ft rope doubtless intended to be generous and allowed an extra 13ft as a 'safe margin'; it was clear that because the rope was too long by this amount, it had at some time, when the jib had been fully raised, run onto the worm wheel and had been crushed there by the worm itself, receiving damage that ultimately caused it to break.

The greatest railway feature in Scotland is undoubtedly the Forth Bridge, opened in 1890, and most tourists to Edinburgh include it in their itinerary if they can, as it is only about nine miles away. In the mid 1930s I crossed the bridge several times on engine footplates which was then the best way of seeing it; today anyone can enjoy a similar trip by taking a front seat in a diesel multiple unit (dmu) train; with a total length of nearly $1\frac{3}{4}$ miles it is certainly a grand bridge. The main structure consists of three double cantilevers known as Queensferry, Inch Garvie and Fife, with a central girder between each pair to give a clear shipping headway of 150ft; each cantilever tower is 360ft above high water level. The main structure is approached by the South Viaduct, 660yd in length, and the North Viaduct of 322yd; the adjacent cantilevers are not fixed to the approach viaduct piers and do not rest or impose any weight on them, the ends of these cantilevers each having a counterpoise weight of 1,000 tons to balance half the weight of the central girder carried by the opposite cantilever. The deck supporting the Up and Down tracks is called the continuous viaduct and rests on substantial trestle girders which in turn stand on the cantilevers' lower booms. There is a continuous parapet called a wind fence along each side of the deck, of stout steel lattice and with a heavy teak handrail along the top. Few people have been sufficiently privileged, as I have on several occasions, to walk across the bridge, which has a manned watchman's cabin at its southern end; anyone wishing to study the steelwork can do so from below quite readily, however, at the north end where a roadway leads to open ground beneath the outermost cantilever. To be on or beneath the bridge is an awe-inspiring experience.

But there the wonders cease. The Forth Bridge designers made few provisions for easy and ready maintenance; in the 1880s the needs for such facilities hardly seemed to occur to engineers. At every place where the steelwork has to be repaired or painted, except on the deck or within the cantilever tubes, scaffolding of some sort has first to be erected and taken down again afterwards, or else men must sling cradles which they enter by temporarily secured ladders. The lower booms of the continuous viaduct's longitudinal girders are joined by light cross girders some 20ft apart which carry a two-plank catwalk, 1ft 10in wide with thin wire ropes along each side to serve as handrails; it is reached by stairways leading down from hatchways set at intervals along the deck and it is the only means of access to a great deal of the bridge's steelwork. Anyone who goes onto the bridge thus needs to be perfectly capable of working at great heights and maybe in any weather without fear of giddiness or loss of balance, and this applies to the civil engineers and supervisors as well as the workmen.

A team of some 80 men maintain the bridge; they are mostly blacksmiths, platers, riveters, painters, scaffolders and joiners, and all seem quite accustomed to walking about on the steel members or on planks anything from 100 to 350ft above the water; accidents are rare but, regrettably, there have been a few incidents of men losing their foothold and falling into the sea. When men are engaged amidst the steelwork a small lifeboat is always moored beneath them and they are in radio communication with the coxwain. All shouting and calling in the course of ordinary work is prohibited among men on the bridge, by mutual consent; shouts are reserved as an additional means of alerting the boatman and others should a man fall into the water.

I have investigated two such accidents, both fatal, and it was necessary for me to see as best I could the places from where the men fell; having endured and survived some four years of steady air raids at Lowestoft I am not now scared of many things but to have to step along that terrible 1ft 10in catwalk as I did during my first Inquiry, clinging to the thin wire ropes in a horrid wind and with a choppy sea and flying spray 150ft below, really started the flutters in my stomach. The bridge inspector who went with me led the way at his own pace, striding along the planks with his hands in his pockets with somewhat alarming comments such as 'aye, it can blaw up here in winter 'til ye can scarce hold on, and the sea doun there is aft sae rough they canna put oot yon lifeboat'! However, he assured me that the catwalk planks were sound, having recently been renewed; the accident into which I was inquiring had, indeed, occurred during the repair work, a man having slipped when walking along one of the trestle girders in order to catch the end of a rope being let down from the deck. He was rescued by the lifeboat within three minutes, despite the fast currents and the difficulties in manoeuvring the craft, but he did not survive.

In the other case a man slid off a huge stage that was suspended beneath the deck by chains; it tipped suddenly when one of the chains, which had been attached to a wind fence by a hitch instead of by a more positive shackle and pin, loosened and came adrift. The unfortunate man disappeared into the water before the lifeboat could reach him.

The other great Scottish bridge is, of course, that over the Tay Estuary, famous for all time because of the disaster of Sunday 28 December 1879 when the first Tay Bridge collapsed with the loss of 75 lives; the casualty list was the worst in any railway accident in the British Isles up to then and was not exceeded until the Armagh catastrophe 10 years later. The first bridge was designed by the engineer Thomas Bouch who, as a young man, created the world's first train ferries to take wagons across the Forth and Tay estuaries; he also planned several railways in the north of England and designed a number of railway bridges and viaducts. Before long the wagon ferries, although successful, became unable to cope with the steadily increasing traffic and Bouch was asked by the North British Railway to carry out the bridging of the Tay.

The bridge was started in 1871 and took seven years to build. Its deck, carrying a single line, was supported by 85 piers; 13 of its openings were for shipping and had lattice spans, known as the High Girders, with the track running through them, 88ft above high water level. Eleven of the High Girders were 245ft in length, the other two being a little less. The remaining openings had lattice spans with the track on top of them. Of the supporting piers 14 were of brick but the rest, including those carrying the High Girders, were of cast iron columns, filled with Portland cement and braced to one another, six columns to a pier. Both the brick and cast iron piers were of almost uniform width from bottom to top, the pier footings in the river bed being too small to permit the columns from being spread adequately at their bases for stability; the result was, apart from curves at each end, a straight but slender and very wobbly bridge, 3,465yd in length. The iron lattice girders were made at Middlesbrough but all the cast iron columns were produced in a temporary foundry set up at Wormit, at the bridge's southern end. They were tubular, 18in in diameter, and the iron was intended to be an inch thick but the foundry was badly supervised and the work slovenly; some of the columns were thinner on one side than the other and some had cracks and blow holes in the iron which the foundrymen filled with wax and iron filings so that they would not be noticed. Many of the lugs on the columns to which braces and struts were to be pinned were weak, and their holes, instead of being drilled, were fashioned at the time of casting and were inaccurate.

Bouch had made little if any allowance in his design for side wind effects but up to that time few engineers had regarded wind to be a serious factor; great minster and cathedral towers had stood in all weathers so why shouldn't a bridge pier? He forgot that the further north one goes the more tempestuous the winter storms are likely to be, and his bridge was further north than any previous similar structure. On 29 May 1878 the bridge was opened and thereafter trains, controlled by the staff and ticket system, crossed it until 28 December the following year without incident, except that during that period a few of the cast iron columns developed cracks and had to be bound with iron straps, and many of the bracings worked loose.

On the fatal evening a great storm developed and by the time the 5.27pm train from Burntisland to Dundee was leaving Wormit a westerly gale was raging along the estuary. Even with the bridge unladen, the piers, already weak due to slack bracing between the badly made columns, were probably shaking in the wind that beat against them and the sides of the girders; when the train, of five four-wheeled coaching vehicles and one six-wheeler, reached the fourth and fifth High Girders the wind pressure on both the girders and the carriage sides proved too much. The two spans toppled seawards with the train inside them as the columns beneath gave way, bringing down the remaining eleven High Girders as well. There were no survivors and only 46 of the 75 bodies were recovered.

After the catastrophe the construction of the present bridge, much stronger and with dual tracks, was begun almost at once; the main girders that remained on the piers of Bouch's bridge were built into the new structure which was opened in 1887. The coaches were retrieved and the locomotive, NBR No 224, was also hauled out of the Tay, repaired at Cowlairs, returned to traffic with a new number, 1192, and kept at work until 1919. Not only was she 'The Tay Bridge Engine' but also the first 4–4–0 inside cylinder bogie tender engine to be built in Britain and, presumably in the world.

The Board of Trade's file of papers on the Inquiry has been preserved by the Department of Transport, among its documents being the original telegram by which the NBR's General Manager reported the accident. British Railways still possesses a small exhibition of Tay Bridge relics, including the tickets collected from the doomed train's passengers when the last scheduled stop was made, at Leuchars Junction.

The Tay Bridge failure appears to have put the BOT in a quandary, the structure and its track having been examined by an IO shortly before the opening for passenger traffic. Why, people asked, had he so readily given his approval for the running of trains along a bridge that was of inadequate strength and contained faulty materials? Why did the Board's inspectors not supervise both the design of the bridge and its construction? The President of the BOT, realising that these challenges had to be answered, issued a minute dated 15 July 1880 in which the limits of an IO's duty were made clear. The duty was to inspect *new* railways and if the Inspector reported that the opening of a line would be attended by danger to the travelling public because of its incompleteness the BOT then had powers to postpone the opening; Parliament had not, however, given the BOT powers to inspect or superintend works of building or erecting. An IO could not, the Minute emphasised, be expected in the course of his examinations to look for and discover faults in the materials and workmanship of a structure when the defects were not visible by the time the structure was finished and painted, Parliament not having committed such responsibilities to him. And furthermore, the Minute added, if the BOT were to be held responsible for the design of railway structures and the superintendence of their construction it would need to employ a huge staff of engineers, draughtsmen and other technical personnel, and such an arrangement would be contrary to the principle of allowing railways to be built and operated with the minimum of Government interference.

And so the basic rule that the planning, design and construction of a railway and all its works must always be the responsibility of the railway's own engineers, and of consulting engineers and contractors who may be engaged by them, continued and has remained the Inspectorate's principle down to the present day. Nevertheless, when the Forth railway bridge was being built the Inspectorate did not take any chances; IOs examined the work of construction every three months!

I have twice held Inquiries into fatalities which occurred during Tay Bridge repairs; as on the Forth Bridge, almost everything has to be done from scaffolding and cradles. A longitudinal gangway under the deck is a stouter affair than the Forth Bridge catwalk, being about 3ft wide and with a substantial handrail along one side only; I kept very close to that handrail indeed when I had to walk along that gangway, with the Tay waters about 70ft below!

The first Tay Bridge accident that I investigated happened in October 1963 and was another case of a stage that fell when tackle suspending it gave way, due in this case to mishandling. A rescue launch, manned by two boatmen, is always moored close to any place where men are working on the bridge, elsewhere than on the deck; when this accident occurred the boatmen responded very promptly but two men who had fallen into the water vanished beneath the surface before the launch could be brought close enough to haul them out.

My second visit was in 1967 when a considerable stretch of the bridge was being infested by vast hordes of starlings. Millions of these revolting birds were scouring the fields of the Scottish Lowlands every day for food and then converging on the bridge at sundown to roost amongst the steel members, and all attempts to dislodge them for good had proved absolutely ineffective. Their droppings accumulated on the girders and the gangway to a depth, in places, of six inches; hours of labour were being spent almost daily in scraping away this slimy and disgusting deposit. A painter slipped on a patch of bird fouling in the course of handling scaffold timbers and fell; although the rescue launch was at the scene within two or three minutes he, too, disappeared into the water before the boatmen could seize him. When nuisances reach plague proportions it becomes extremely difficult to apply remedies but after this tragedy the Civil Engineer did his best to improve his men's safety by installing propane operated bird scarers at places where work was to be started and by appointing men to clean the areas as well as they could by applying chemicals.

Left: Diesel locomotives suffer badly in collisions. A typical example. *Below:* Scene of the Hatfield accident on 23 March 1968.

Left: Vandalism. A fragment of the damage costing £10,000 to make good, done by children in BR sidings. A case for the psychiatrist or the birch? (*British Railways Board*). *Below:* A junction nameboard at York, one of many set up following the author's recommendation.

Holgate Jn

10 A Chapter of Accidents

I am not going to describe scores of accidents and the Inquiries into their causes, nor to display numerous illustrations of dreadful accident scenes; summaries of a few of my cases are sufficient to depict the work of the SEI.

Although IOs normally investigate passenger train accidents, in 1964 they were all so preoccupied with Inquiries and other work that when the 6.40am steam-hauled up passenger train from Machynlleth struck one of the gates at Cil-Cwrgan Public Level Crossing, on the Aberystwyth to Shrewsbury route, the Inquiry that was ordered was given to me. The crossing lay on the single track line between Newtown and Abermule stations, less than a mile from the place where in 1921 the notorious head-on collision between two trains had occurred due to mishandling of a token. The crossing was small, a narrow roadway over the track leading to the village of Lanmerewig, and it had only one 15ft gate on each side, normally kept across the highway and locked by a ground frame lever; the resident crossing keeper dwelt in a cottage close at hand. The crossing was protected by up and down home signals each 500yd away and also worked from the ground frame; they were normally kept lowered and had both to be restored to danger before the gates' unlocking lever could be pulled; once the gates were released the signals could not be cleared until the gates were properly relocked in position across the roadway. In clear weather both signals were visible from the crossing.

The crossing's protection was thus adequate and there was a

pointer and dial indicator which showed either that the line was clear or, if not, whether an up or a down train was approaching. Before letting road traffic go over the line the keeper had first to inspect the indicator and check that it was not showing the approach of a down train or, if it showed that an up train was coming, to be certain that the Newtown's 'train entering section' signal had not yet been repeated on a bell outside the cottage; it was then in order to put the two home signals to danger and then to unlock and swing the gates across the track.

It was a foggy September morning when, at about 8.0am and as the train was getting near the crossing, having passed the up signal which was at 'clear', the two enginemen saw the keeper attempting to swing one of the gates out of the train's path; a few moments later the engine destroyed the gate, the keeper being killed at the same time. If there was a road vehicle at the gates it had vanished by the time the train had been stopped and the trainmen had run back. I decided that the keeper, after seeing the indicator's 'up train on line' but unaware that two bell beats denoting 'train entering section' had rung, put the signals to danger and released the gate locks, and I also concluded that the locomotive had just passed the up signal when its indication changed. In fog, when the signal was invisible from the crossing, it would have been better had the keeper, after reversing the signals, then waited half a minute or so before unlocking the gates, to allow time for a train that might be drawing close to go by, but it had not occurred to anyone to include such briefing in the keeper's instructions. The Report being my first to be printed by the Stationery Office, I was rather proud of it.

The Report had scarcely been published when I was given another crossing case to investigate, again in Wales and this time in Anglesey. At the crossing the up and down tracks of the Holyhead main line were intersected by a lane leading from the A5 road to a couple of farms and a house or two; the need to open the gates to road traffic occurred no more than a dozen or so times a day. The crossing keeper relied on a pair of indicators that showed whether the lines were clear or otherwise and the crossing regulations stipulated that if either indicator showed 'train approaching' or 'train in section' the gates were not to be moved from their positions across the roadway until the train had gone by. At about noon one day in May a car halted at the gates which could not be opened, however, because the up indicator showed that an eastbound train was coming. The train went by but the keeper then forgot to look at the other indicator and so remained unaware that it had changed and that a down train was on the way; the gates were then swung away from the roadway but as the car began to cross the rails a down, westbound, train struck it, pushing it nearly 300yd along the track. I felt considerable sympathy for the crossing keeper who was nearly 70 years of age and who had never, I was told, made a mistake before; I was, however, a little critical when local railway officers claimed to me that the keeper's inability to read or write was something that they had never previously discovered. When an inspector told me that it had been his duty to test the keeper's competency every two years and indeed to visit the crossing seven or eight times a year my criticisms became more pronounced; as the crossing keeper spoke only Welsh and the inspector knew no Welsh at all the tests must have been pretty superficial to say the least. However, the printed instructions for working the crossing, though only in English, were very simple and the keeper had heard them read and explained by someone who was bilingual.

By the time I had dealt with these and a few more similar cases I came to appreciate that few level crossings are alike, except those worked by a signalman from a box alongside. The arrangements of the gates and the means of locking them vary considerably; so do the methods of protection, some having semaphore home signals and others only distant signals, while yet others have levers that put colour-light signals to danger on the approach side, and some do not have any signals at all. On single lines one lever may control both up and down signals. Some crossings have indicators showing the state of the line continuously and at others the keeper must get an adjacent signalman's permission by telephone before letting road traffic pass over the railway. Many keepers have a cabin like a tiny signalbox but at crossings used only a few times a day they are more likely to reside in a cottage close by and need to be called by a bell or telephone. Almost every crossing has its own little set of local operating instructions.

There are in the main four types of level crossing, these being 1) public crossings where the railway intersects a highway, 2) occupation crossings, which occur where a private road or lane leads from a highway to premises such as a few cottages, a farm or factory on the far side of the line, 3) accommodation crossings provided where a railway divides a farm or estate and which is solely for the landowner's private use, to enable his farm animals or implements to be taken over the tracks, and 4) footpath crossings, found where a public footpath goes over the line. All public crossings have official names and, apart from the 230 or so equipped with automatic half barriers, are invariably worked either by a signalman or keeper or, in a few cases, by a signalman from a distance who observes road traffic conditions by closed circuit television equipment. Occupation crossings are usually manned but may as an alternative be operated by the red/green light system, the road users working the gates themselves when the lights are green and being able to telephone to one of the local signalmen if need be. Accommodation crossings have wooden or steel tubular gates hung so as to open away from the tracks, it being the landowner's responsibility to keep them closed and fastened when not in use. They are or should be installed where a good view can be obtained along the line each way and positioned with an ample 'bay' of ground between each gate and the nearest rail. Footpaths across the tracks are usually in the form of narrow timber or earth walkways, stiles generally being provided in the railway fence with 'beware of trains' notices alongside them.

The last occasion when a locomotive boiler exploded, by which I mean blew up and disintegrated, was at Buxton on 11 November 1921 when, owing to maladjustment and consequent jamming of the safety valves on LNWR Engine No 134, some three months after the locomotive had been given a general overhaul by a contractor because of the company's inability to deal with all its wartime arrears of locomotive repairs at its Crewe works, the boiler burst, destroying the rest of the engine as well. But there have been cases since of fireboxes giving way because of shortage of water and of boilers being punctured by connecting rods that have broken or come to pieces; there have also been sudden failures of tubes, steam pipes or boiler fittings, and I had such an accident to investigate in Scotland. The engine concerned was No 90771, one of the WD 2–10–0 freight class similar to the engine used on the Rugby Testing Plant, with a boiler containing three parallel 3in steel water tubes running fore and aft in the firebox from the water space beneath the firehole doorway to the firebox's front water space. These tubes were about 6ft 6in in length, bowed slightly upwards, and served as supports for the brick arch; they had been tightened by a tool called a tube expander where they went through the firebox plates which were of steel, not copper. An expander is a barrel having an easy taper and containing perhaps seven or eight rollers; when it is inserted into the end of a tube and then revolved gently by a ratchet handle it causes a gradual increase in the tube's diameter.

Early one December morning in 1962, No 90771 was drawing a freight train out of a siding at Elderslie, near Glasgow, when one of the water tubes in the firebox suddenly came adrift from the firebox's front plate; steam at about 225 lb/sq in filled the firebox in a second or two and then burst into the engine cab, carrying firebox flames with it. Both driver and fireman were terribly scalded and the driver died a few days later. I made a very thorough examination of the boiler which involved crawling about inside the firebox and soon saw what had happened. The tube that slipped out of its hole in the front plate had, of course, been properly fitted and tightened by expanding when first put in but then, each time the engine returned to its shed after working a train, and once the fire had been thrown out, the tube cooled and contracted a little more rapidly than the rest of the boiler which caused it to withdraw ever so slightly from the firebox plate. When the rest of the boiler then cooled the firebox contraction bent the already-curved tube slightly further upwards; this process evidently repeated itself day after day until the tube was on the verge of dropping out of the plate altogether, when some small jolt of the engine then shook it out of place. I would have condemned all such tubes at once but I was told at my Inquiry that BR had already decided to take them out of every 2–10–0 engine.

When the accident occurred the tube did not drop completely away from the 3in opening in the water space; had it done so the whole of the boiler contents would have emptied into the firebox and cab with such violence as to amount to an explosion. It fell only a quarter to half an inch, leaving an opening amounting to perhaps one square inch in area but, with steam at 225 lb/sq in, this was sufficient to put anyone on the footplate in immediate and deadly peril. It behoves the management of railway preservation organisations, tourist steam railways, and working museums to bear in mind that when a boiler holds steam under pressure a sudden small leak or the failure of a pipe can release a terrible amount of steam at high temperature. Although water boils and becomes steam in a saucepan at 212°F, at 225 lb/sq in its temperature is 390°F; moreover, once such steam escapes from a boiler into the open air it remains as steam until it has cooled to 212°F *and* has shed all its latent heat; only then will it begin to condense into water which, however, will still be at ordinary boiling point. In warm weather cooling will take all the longer and the fate of anyone getting caught and enveloped in such steam can be left to the imagination.

Buchanan Street station in Glasgow has gone now but on 6 September 1962 Gresley's 4–6–2 Pacific No 60094, *Colorado*, collided at the platform approaches with an ex LMS locomotive, No 45161, and I investigated the incident. The station used to be the terminus for the Glasgow to Aberdeen trains and in 1962 a few ex LNER Pacifics were put onto the line because their great power and steaming capacity enabled them to take heavy trains with ease up the six mile ascents of about 1 in 100 on each side of Gleneagles. Some were allocated to St Rollox shed and the two mile descent from there to Buchanan Street required them to travel tender leading through a horrible wet and smoky tunnel on a falling gradient of 1 in 79.

Colorado, like others of her class, had a vacuum brake, with two vacuum cylinders on the engine and two on the tender; they were known as 'separate cylinders', enlargement of the space above each piston being achieved by connections to a separate vacuum chamber which was a large steel tank on the tender top, at the back. The brake fitting in the cab had an application handle and two steam-operated vacuum-raising ejectors of unequal power; the larger ejector was for releasing the brake and the smaller one was for the continuous maintenance of the vacuum against the tiny leaks that always occur unavoidably where there are joints and connections amongst vacuum brake pipes and fittings. When the train pipe was full of air and the brake hard on the smaller ejector maintained the vacuum on the 'chamber side' which means above the pistons and in the vacuum chamber; it was the driver's duty to start the smaller ejector when getting his engine ready at the shed and to keep it in operation all the time the engine was at work. The ejectors were not designed to exhaust the air totally from the train pipe and the vacuum chamber but provided a two-thirds vacuum or, in scientific terms, a vacuum equivalent to 21in of mercury.

The engine left St Rollox shed with the driver, fireman and five other men in the cab, four of whom should not have been there. On the way to the station the vacuum brake was found to be almost completely useless, the driver could not prevent the engine from passing a signal at danger and by the time it ran out of the tunnel its speed was about 20mph; on seeing that a collision with the other engine was inevitable most of the men jumped off, one of them losing his life. The brake was defective, the rolling ring in one of the tender cylinders which provided the air tight seal between the piston and the cylinder wall having slipped partly over the piston head; this left a $\frac{1}{16}$in gap a foot long so that when a brake application was attempted the air from the train pipe entered the space above the piston, and above the other three pistons because all the spaces were pipe-connected, and the atmospheric pressure had little or no effect beneath the pistons as a result. Nevertheless, the smaller ejector was powerful enough to have overcome, or almost overcome, such an 'internal leak' as it is called and my conclusion was that although the driver had no doubt thought that the smaller ejector steam valve was open he had not seen to it that the ejector was working properly.

Colorado had not been at St Rollox depot very long before the accident and I found it somewhat disturbing to hear that an engine fitted with the vacuum brake had been put into the hands of a driver whose experience until then had been entirely with steam braked engines; indeed, this contributed to the incident. Just because, on nationalisation, all engines had come under one ownership, it did not follow by any means that it was wise to send them to sheds indiscriminately and to place classes of engine in the charge of drivers who had never handled such types before. *Colorado* was badly damaged by the collision and that was the end of it; it never went back into traffic.

On 10 November 1965 fire broke out at a large petroleum depot in Carlisle. Petrol and diesel oil consigned to the depot arrived in tank wagons which British Railways staff shunted into the depot sidings; the petroleum company's men then coupled them to the depot's pipe lines by large hoses. Just before 8.0am, when it was nearly daylight, 18 loaded wagons of petrol and oil were pushed into the depot, the shunter signalling to the locomotive driver by a paraffin hand lamp. A hose was put onto one of the petrol wagons immediately and discharging was begun; unfortunately no one noticed that a valve further along the pipe line had been left open and petrol was soon pouring from it onto the ground. Petrol fumes quickly saturated the air and the shunter's hand lamp flame caused a flashover that set the spilt petrol on fire; a 20ft sheet of flame shot up in a matter of seconds.

Fortunately the shunter escaped with only slight burns and no one else was hurt; the Fire Brigade arrived within four minutes and soon extinguished the blaze, after about 700 gallons of petrol had been lost. One tank wagon had most of its paint burned off but luckily it held diesel oil; had its contents been petrol the heat would probably have burst it, causing a fire which could well have ignited every storage tank in the depot and imperilled much of Carlisle itself. The incident marked the end of the paraffin lamp era; at the Inquiry which I held I would have recommended the use of only electric hand lamps in future for railwaymen but the BRB decided on this before I had even finished investigating.

In 1968 two serious freight accidents occurred within 12 days, both on the East Coast main line and I held an Inquiry into each. The first was just to the south of Peterborough on a freight line worked by the Permissive Block system. A 'permissive' section between two signal boxes is one to which a second train may be admitted although it is still occupied by the previous train; the principle enables trains to get along the route as far as they can towards the place where the train ahead may have been detained temporarily. If a train has not yet cleared a section when a second, or even a third or fourth train is about to enter it the driver of each following train must be warned, and as the rules stood at the time this was done by keeping the starting signal at danger until the driver had brought his train nearly to a stand, and then clearing it; having been so warned, it was then the driver's duty to proceed at reduced speed and to keep a good lookout for the train in front. Only freight or mineral lines are allowed to be worked in this manner; all passenger lines must be worked by the Absolute Block system and if in emergency a passenger train has to travel along a 'permissive' line it must be signalled under Absolute Block regulations.

Just to the south of Peterborough station an Up (southbound) Goods Loop, worked by Permissive Block, diverged from the Up Main passenger line at Crescent Junction signalbox. At about 9.0pm on 11 March an up train of hopper wagons, without a brake van at the rear, entered the Up Goods Loop but was detained by a home signal $1\frac{1}{4}$ miles further on. Then another hopper wagon train, hauled by Type 4 diesel locomotive No 115, entered the loop, the signal controlling entry not having been cleared until the train had come almost to a halt. It seems, however, that the conductor driver, who was handling the controls, forgot that he was entering a 'permissive' line and did not appreciate the significance of the signal check; he did not curb his speed and when a minute or two later he saw the tail light on the back of the previous train he assumed somewhat casually that the train was not on the Loop. By the time he realised that the train was, in fact, on his line it was too late; there was a violent 20mph collision and No 115's front was completely stove in. The driver and his conductor, I regret, were killed and the secondman was trapped and injured by the crushed steelwork; it took ten hours to cut him free.

The RI had advised the railways, some eight years earlier, that drivers needed better and unmistakable indications of whether 'permissive' lines that they are entering are clear or occupied, and in many places the warning were already being given by miniature 'calling-on' arms below the full sized arms of the signals controlling admission; if the line was clear the main signal arm was cleared but if not the calling-on arm was cleared instead. Shortly after the Peterborough accident a calling-on arm was installed on the Up Loop signal at Crescent Junction.

The second freight train accident was at Hatfield when, at about 5.0am, a train scheduled to stop on the Down Goods line entered it at excessive speed; travelling at about 30mph, it then continued onto a shunting spur and collided violently with an overline bridge abutment. The locomotive was very heavily damaged and nine of the wagons behind it were completely destroyed; both the driver and his secondman were killed outright and the reason why the train was allowed to travel at such a speed that it could not be stopped on the Goods line must for all time remain unknown. The tracks were buried in grain spilled from the smashed vehicles; every Trafalgar Square pigeon hastened to Hatfield, remaining several days to feast.

In 1969 head-on collisions on single track freight routes called long sidings began to occur. These tracks were once parts of main lines that had been closed, having been left in place to maintain access to factories, mines or quarries along the routes; they were not provided with any token system of operation, the RI's requirements for working single lines not applying to lines which are not passenger routes. In ordinary sidings, to and fro movements are conducted by shunters who avoid collisions by exercising care and vigilance, and it seems to have been expected that care and vigilance would prevent things from going wrong on the 'long sidings' as well. Events proved, however, that more positive control was necessary if casualties were to be avoided. At least one of the 'long sidings' extended four miles.

I investigated four 'long siding' collisions all of which were fairly similar; two locomotives running light, or a locomotive and a train, met head-on at a place where the line was sharply curved and the view along it very restricted. On one line the trainmen were expected to look after themselves once they were on the 'long siding', and on the other three there were various instructions about getting permission by telephone from the far end before taking a train onto the single track; in each case I recommended that there ought to be much more substantial methods of working the lines than shunters' vigilance or exchanged telephone calls, for unless staff who have to organise train operation adhere strictly to properly prescribed forms of wording, telephone messages can become very muddled and uncertain. As a result of my recommendations the working of these lines was made safe and sound, either by introducing a train staff or by interlocking the signals controlling access to the lines to prevent conflicting movements. It is all very well to tell men to be mindful and watchful, and to do what the Rules say, but caution alone is insufficient for working a single line; the consequences of a collision can well be so grave that working methods which will *ensure* that the line never has more than one train at a time are absolutely essential. Fortunately, none of these four collisions caused any bad injuries.

Runaway trains have featured in several of my Inquiries. In 1970 a 22 wagon coal train ran seven miles out of control down a gradient of about 1 in 60 on the historic Stanhope & Tyne route; on being diverted at about 40mph by trap points into a sand drag the locomotive and most of the vehicles became derailed, piled into a heap and were wrecked. The train began to prove too much for the locomotive shortly after leaving Annfield and at the next two signalboxes it passed signals at danger. The signalmen could have sent a 'train running away on right line' message to the signalmen ahead in good time had all their equipment been in order; the trap points could probably then have been closed, allowing the train onto the main line where it would have lost its impetus. Unfortunately some of the copper telegraph and telephone wires along the S&T line had been cut down by thieves a few days before and stolen for the sake of the metal, rendering the block bells unworkable and leaving the signalmen to despatch their trains on the time interval system that the regulations permit in such circumstances. A temporary communicating cable laid as soon as the theft was discovered was destroyed almost immediately by thieves or vandals.

I found that the runaway would not have occurred had the trainmen applied and 'pinned down' sufficient wagon hand brake levers at Annfield when the train started but this important measure was neglected; the incident was, however, an example of what determined destruction of railway equipment by thieves can lead to, causing in this case not only a huge amount of damage but also the loss of a trainman's life.

A few months later I had another case before me, initiated by the theft of communication wires; it occurred between Apperley Junction and Kirkstall, near Leeds. Late at night a man went onto the line, swarmed up a telegraph pole and cut about 20 wires, stealing some and leaving the rest entangled on the ground. This put all the block signalling equipment out of action and the signalmen's telephones as well; the Apperley Junction signalman discovered that his apparatus had broken down when he attempted to dispatch a goods train to Kirkstall, four miles away. He allowed the train to go forward after telling the driver that 'time interval working' was in force and instructing him to proceed cautiously; the driver's duty, then, was to work his train so that he could stop short of any train that might be ahead and not to assume if he saw cleared signals ahead that the line was, in fact, vacant for his train.

The goods train set off and 13 minutes later an empty dmu train arrived at Apperley Junction, going the same way. It waited at the signalbox for about a minute, and the driver was told that the block instruments had failed, that he was to proceed at caution, and that the previous train had gone 14 minutes earlier. The dmu train then entered the section and at first the driver kept its speed in check but on seeing the Kirkstall distant signal at clear he wrongly concluded that he could now work his train normally and increased its speed to about 40mph. As a result the train caught up with the goods train, which had not quite reached Kirkstall, and although the dmu driver suddenly saw three red lights ahead his train's speed was such that a violent collision was unavoidable. The goods train guard was fatally injured. Perhaps in those parts there is a man who still carries the knowledge that his mean and despicable theft and the damage that he caused to railway fixtures led to another man's death and maybe left some children fatherless as well. British Railways, however, agreed with my recommendation that a distant signal should not be cleared in such circumstances and altered the regulations accordingly.

Trains, running at speed on rails as they do, are particularly vulnerable to interference and anyone who tampers with railway apparatus, however slight their meddling may be, exposes both passengers and personnel to grave risks and if caught should in my view be rigorously punished. There are men today, it seems, who are not going to be deterred from thieving and vandalism on railways except in my view by the knowledge that such wickedness is likely to bring them into personal acquaintance with the cane or the birch.

173

After an end-on collision on a Permissive Block line in North London I persuaded the BRB's officers to improve their instructions. The method laid down by rule for warning drivers of a train on the line ahead was to bring their trains 'nearly to a stand' at the starting signal but when I investigated this collision I found that the following train had been stopped and detained. This *may* have given the driver the impression that he was being kept back until the section ahead was clear, although this remains unconfirmed as he lost his life in the accident. Nevertheless, the regulation was altered on my recommendation and now reads 'stopped or brought nearly to a stand'.

Sometimes, instead of following an EI's recommendation, the BRB introduces an alternative remedy that is just as good. At one of the public level crossings where I have held Inquiries the crossing name was not displayed, which I considered to be a deficiency that might lead to difficulties should trainmen require to identify the site in an emergency. It was decided, however, that to put up name boards at all the crossings that lacked them would be too costly; instead, all crossings were listed by name in the General Appendix's next issue. The staff had never previously had a comprehensive level crossing inventory.

Two contractor's men were lucky to escape with minor injuries when in 1973 a trestle on which they were standing, beneath a bridge at Wigan, was knocked over by a dmu train. Three junctions close together near the bridge, and all worked from the power signalbox at Warrington, were known loosely as Springs Branch; when a circular proclaimed that, on a prescribed day, the Up Slow line would be closed to traffic for engineering purposes southwards from Springs Branch, the contractor's men took advantage of the situation, believing their work site to be within the closed stretch. As it happened, the closed length of line fell short of the bridge and both tracks through the bridge were open to traffic. I discovered at my Inquiry that many of the people concerned in the affair did not know which of the three junctions was, in fact, Springs Branch and I realised that whereas in the past the identity of a junction was invariably established very clearly by the name of the manual signalbox controlling it, junctions worked from centralised power signalboxes miles away were left nameless. I recommended that, to avoid confusion in future, all junctions controlled from a distance should have nameboards alongside them and this suggestion of mine has been followed; today nearly all such junctions are so marked, and the nameboards can usually be seen without difficulty from the train by both crew and interested passengers.

Extensive travelling has enabled me to see many railway features quite unconnected with any official duties, and some have been the fairly numerous fragments of railways that were begun but never completed. One of the largest is the discarded Mistley, Thorpe & Walton Railway, in Essex, with three or four miles of cuttings and bridge works, unfinished and abandoned in 1868. Further north, at Debenham, bridge abutments alongside the B1077 road and half a mile of railway can be seen, left unfinished by the Mid-Suffolk Light Railway. Near Kirklington, North Yorkshire, traces of the Northern Counties Union Railway can be found; the intended mileage of this system was 127 but only three miles were ever made, in 1846, and then given up.

Tadcaster still possesses a deserted eleven-arch viaduct over the River Wharfe, built in 1848 by George Hudson as part of a Leeds to York line that never materialised. Some three miles east of Cheltenham and on the northern side of the A40 road, about 200yd of embankment followed by a similar amount of cutting buried in undergrowth represent all that was ever made, in 1865, of the East Gloucestershire Railway before the company gave up. About a mile to the south of Pauntley, a Gloucestershire village (and Dick Whittington's birthplace), lie a few traces representing the pathetic start of the Worcester, Dean Forest & Monmouth Railway, a company that was wound up in 1869. In Sussex a couple of miles of the abandoned Ouse Valley Railway are visible to the north of Lindfield. Most railway students know, of course, of the greatest abandoned work of all, the huge

Bordesley Viaduct across the streets of Birmingham, which was finished in 1853 but has never carried a train.

By 8 November 1974 I had reached the age of 65 and had to relinquish the SEI's desk and chair to a successor; I did, however, remain in the RI in a lower capacity four years more and when that came to an end I was able to sit down and write this book. And now my $52\frac{1}{2}$ years of work and recreation as a railwayman are ended. I began my service when Britain's biggest steam locomotives were coming into their own – the LNER Pacifics, the Royal Scots, the Lord Nelsons, and the GWR Kings – when almost all signalling was semaphore and mechanically operated and when fogsignalmen were posted at most signals on days of reduced visibility. It was a time when almost every line in the British Isles carried passengers, and when all permanent way work was done by hand. In my $52\frac{1}{2}$ years I have seen extensive closures on the one hand and over 600 miles of main line electrified on the overhead system on the other. The main line steam engine has been superseded by the diesel and electric locomotive, almost all the principal routes have been relaid with continuous welded rails and nearly all track repair work is now done by machinery, giving our passenger lines standards of accuracy impossible by manual methods. Signalling has been revolutionised and trains are attaining speeds never imagined possible in 1926. What railway developments, I wonder, will today's new entrants to the railway see during the next 50 years?

Thus I bid farewell to the Department of Transport and to railway work in general; the time has at last come to put away the trains which have been so much a part of my life so happily and for so long.